Solutions Manual
to accompany

PREPARATION FOR CALCULUS
Third Edition

S.L. Salas
C.G. Salas

John Wiley & Sons

New York/Chichester
Brisbane/Toronto
Singapore

ISBN 0-471-81894-1
Printed in the United States of America

10 9 8 7 6 5 4 3 2 1

SECTION 1.1

1.

$$\begin{array}{c}
\overline{|||||||} \\
{-4}{-1}0\;\tfrac{1}{2}\;12\;\tfrac{7}{3}\;3.3
\end{array}$$

2.

$$\begin{array}{c}
\overline{|||||} \\
{-100}{-65}01050
\end{array}$$

3. (a) $\dfrac{34}{5}$ (b) $\dfrac{-9}{4}$ (c) $\dfrac{9}{5}$ (d) $\dfrac{-11}{5}$

    (e) $\dfrac{31}{10}$ (f) $\dfrac{135}{100}$ (g) $\dfrac{3176}{1000}$ (h) $\dfrac{-2115}{1000}$

4. (a) $\dfrac{4}{7}$ (b) $\dfrac{5}{6}$ (c) $\dfrac{5}{7}$ (d) $\dfrac{5}{8}$

    (e) $\dfrac{27}{80}$ (f) $\dfrac{14}{15}$ (g) $\dfrac{1}{81}$ (h) $\dfrac{16}{45}$

5. (a) $\dfrac{5}{6}$ (b) $\dfrac{1}{6}$ (c) $\dfrac{37}{40}$ (d) $\dfrac{23}{45}$

    (e) $\dfrac{2}{9}$ (f) $\dfrac{1}{35}$ (g) $\dfrac{1}{3}$ (h) $\dfrac{1}{10}$

    (i) $\dfrac{5}{36}$ (j) $\dfrac{21}{16}$ (k) $\dfrac{7}{27}$ (l) $14 = \dfrac{14}{1}$

6. (a) 0.56 (b) $0.\overline{3}$ (c) $0.\overline{36}$ (d) 2.75

    (e) $0.\overline{5}$ (f) 0.375 (g) $0.\overline{285714}$ (h) $0.\overline{009}$

7. (a) $\dfrac{4}{9}$ (b) $\dfrac{21}{99}$ (c) $\dfrac{37}{99}$

(d) $10{,}000\,(4.5\overline{123}) = 45{,}123.\overline{123}$

$-10\,(4.5\overline{123}) = 45.\overline{123}$

$\overline{}$

$9{,}990\,(4.5\overline{123}) = 45{,}078 \qquad , \qquad 4.5\overline{123} = \dfrac{45{,}078}{9{,}990}$

(e) $10\,(0.\overline{a_1}) = a_1.\overline{a_1}$

  $-\quad 0.\overline{a_1} = 0.\overline{a_1}$

  $\overline{\quad\quad\quad\quad\quad\quad\quad\quad\quad\quad}$

  $9\,(0.\overline{a_1}) = a_1$, $0.\overline{a_1} = \dfrac{a_1}{9}$

(f) $100\,(0.\overline{a_1 a_2}) = a_1 a_2.\overline{a_1 a_2}$

  $-\quad 0.\overline{a_1 a_2} = 0.\overline{a_1 a_2}$

  $\overline{\quad\quad\quad\quad\quad\quad\quad\quad\quad\quad}$

  $99\,(0.\overline{a_1 a_2}) = a_1 a_2$, $0.\overline{a_1 a_2} = \dfrac{a_1 a_2}{99}$

8. (a) $\dfrac{99}{100}$ (b) $\dfrac{33}{100}$ (c) $\dfrac{1089}{5000}$ (d) $2 = \dfrac{2}{1}$

   (e) $\dfrac{1}{3}$ (f) $1 = \dfrac{1}{1}$ (g) $2 = \dfrac{2}{1}$ (h) $\dfrac{2}{9}$

   (i) $\dfrac{149}{150}$ (j) $\dfrac{49}{150}$ (k) $\dfrac{299}{300}$ (l) $\dfrac{101}{300}$

   (m) $\dfrac{11}{50}$ (n) $\dfrac{99}{50}$ (o) $\dfrac{11}{50}$ (p) $\dfrac{200}{99}$

9.

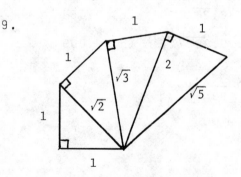

10. No; for example,

  $$\pi + (-\pi) = 0 \quad \text{and} \quad \sqrt{2} \cdot \sqrt{2} = 2.$$

  While π and $\sqrt{2}$ are irrational, 0 and 2 are rational.

11. If 2π were rational, then we could express it as the quotient of two integers:

$$2\pi = \frac{p}{q} \, .$$

But then we could write π itself as the quotient of two integers:

$$\pi = \frac{p}{2q} \, .$$

This would make π rational -- which it is not. ▢

12. $r = 0$; if r were not zero, then $1/r$ would be rational and the product

$$zr \cdot \frac{1}{r} = z$$

would also be rational.

SECTION 1.3

1. $3x - 5y - 2$ 2. $-x + 4$ 3. $3x$

4. $8x + 13y$ 5. $x^2 + 26$ 6. x^2

7. $x - 2xy$ 8. $\frac{1}{4}x + 4y$ 9. $x - y$

10. $5 + 2xy$ 11. $3x + 5$ 12. $-3x + 16$

13. $7x^2 + 3x + 7$ 14. $ac + bc$ 15. $-a + 7b$

16. bx 17. $2xy$ 18. $2x^2z^2$

19. $-6x^2$ 20. $10x$ 21. -3

22. -21 23. 3 24. 6

25. 0 26. -2 27. 1234

28. $18 - 2a$ 29. 2 30. 8

SECTION 1.4

1. $5x^7$ 2. $2a^4b^4$ 3. $8x^6y^3$

4. $-6a^7x^4$ 5. x^3y^3 6. x^3y^4

7. $-27x^6y^{15}$ 8. $5a^4b^5c^2$ 9. $-a^2b^3$

10. $a^2 - b^2$ 11. $a^2 + 2ab + b^2$ 12. $a^2 - 2ab + b^2$

13. $u^3 - a^2u$ 14. $x^2 - 6x + 9$ 15. $x^2 + 4x + 4$

16. $2x^4$ 17. 0 18. 0

19. $2x^{15}$ 20. $u^3 - v^3$ 21. $x^4 - 1$

22. $acx^2 + (ad + bc)xy + bdy^2$ 23. $acx^2 + (bc - ad)xy - bdy^2$

24. $acx^2 - (ad + bc)xy + bdy^2$ 25. $36x^4y^3 - 4x^2y^5$

26. $x^5 + x^3 - x^2 - 1$ 27. $\frac{1}{2}a^2x + \frac{1}{2}a^2x^2$

28. $10x^2 - x^2y^2 - 3xy^2 - y^2$ 29. $-5x^2 - 5x + 5$

30. $6x^5 - 16x^4y - xy^3 + 3y^4$

31. $4x^6 - 8x^5y + 4x^4y^2 - x^2y + 2xy^2 - y^3$

32. $a^3 + 3a^2b + 3ab^2 + b^3$ 33. $a^3 + b^3$

34. $a^3 - 3a^2b + 3ab^2 - b^3$ 35. $a^3 - b^3$

36. rsvp   37. (a) n is even (b) n is odd

38. (a) $\frac{3}{4}$ (b) 0   39. (a) 3   (b) 20

40. (a) 0 (b) $9c^3$ 41. (a) 3   (b) -7

42. (a) 0 (b) $270c^4$ 43. $8ax^3 + 8a^3x$

44. $2x^4 + 12a^2x^2 + 2a^4$ 45. $2x^3 + 22x$

46. $-4x^2 - 16x - 12$ 47. $3x^2 + 21x + 33$

48. $x^6 + 3x^5 + 6x^4 + 7x^3 + 6x^2 + 3x + 1$

49. $x^6 - 3x^5 + 6x^4 - 7x^3 + 6x^2 - 3x + 1$ 50. $1 - x^7$

51. $1 + 2x + 2x^2 + 2x^3 + 2x^4 + 2x^5 + 2x^6 + x^7$

52. $1 - 2x + 2x^2 - 2x^3 + 2x^4 - 2x^5 + 2x^6 - x^7$

53. $1 + x^7$ 54. $1 - x^{n+1}$

SECTION 1.5

1. $x^2 - 1$

2. $x^2 + 2x + 1$

3. $x^2 - 6x + 9$

4. $4x^2 + 4x + 1$

5. $4x^2 - 9$

6. $25x^2 - 10x + 1$

7. $16t^2 + 40t + 25$

8. $16t^2 - 40t + 25$

9. $16t^2 - 25$

10. $x^2 + 4x + 4$

11. $100x^2 + 80xy + 16y^2$

12. $4y^2 - 12xy + 9x^2$

13. $8x^3 + 12x^2 + 6x + 1$

14. $x^2 - 4y^2$

15. $4r^2 + 12rs + 9s^2$

16. $4r^2 - 12rs + 9s^2$

17. $x^3 - 6ax^2 + 12a^2x - 8a^3$

18. $x^3 + 6ax^2 + 12a^2x + 8a^3$

19. $x^2 - \frac{1}{4}$

20. $x^2 + x + \frac{1}{4}$

21. $x^3 + \frac{3}{2}x^2 + \frac{3}{4}x + \frac{1}{8}$

22. $x^3 - \frac{3}{2}x^2 + \frac{3}{4}x - \frac{1}{8}$

23. $\frac{1}{4}x^2 + x + 1$

24. $\frac{1}{4}x^2 - x + 1$

25. $\frac{1}{8}x^3 + \frac{3}{4}x^2 + \frac{3}{2}x + 1$

26. $\frac{1}{8}x^3 - \frac{3}{4}x^2 + \frac{3}{2}x - 1$

27. $\frac{1}{4}x^2 + \frac{1}{3}x + \frac{1}{9}$

28. $x^6 - 3a^2x^4 + 3a^4x^2 - a^6$

29. $x^4 - 16b^4$

30. $x^{12} - 3x^8 + 3x^4 - 1$

31. $x^6 + 3a^2x^4 + 3a^4x^2 + a^6$ 32. $a^6 + 2a^3x^3 + x^6$

33. $a^6 + 3a^4b^2x^2 + 3a^2b^4x^4 + b^6x^6$

SECTION 1.6

1. $3(x + 2)$ 2. $5(x - 20)$ 3. $a(b + 1)$

4. $b(a + c)$ 5. $ab(c + 3)$ 6. $ab(a + b)$

8. $3(x + 4y - 3)$ 9. $2x(x - 2)$

11. $2(x + 2c)(x - 2c)$

13. $(4x + a)(4x - a)$

15. $(x - 2)^2$

17. $(x + 8)^2$ 18. $(x - 8)^2$

4)   20. $(3x - 2)(9x^2 + 6x + 4)$

+ 9)   22. $(5s + 3t)(5s - 3t)$

24. $(x - \frac{1}{2})^2$ 25. $(x + \frac{1}{2})(x - \frac{1}{2})$

+ $\frac{1}{4}y^2$)   27. $(x - \frac{1}{2}y)(x^2 + \frac{1}{2}xy + \frac{1}{4}y^2)$

29. $(ab + cd)(ab - cd)$

+ a^2)   31. $5(x - 3)^2$

32. $2(ax - 2)(a^2x^2 + 2ax + 4)$ 33. $2(x - 2a)(x^2 + 2ax + 4a^2)$

34. $3(x + 11)^2$ 35. $4(x - 5)^2$ 36. $xy(xy^2 - y + 1)$

37. $(9x + 4y)^2$ 38. $(8x + y)(2x - y)$ 39. $3x(5x - 6)$

40. $(d - b)(2x - b - d)$

41. $[(a + c)x + b + d][(a - c)x + b - d]$ 42. $(5s + 3t)^2$

43. $(5s - 3t)^2$ 44. $(ab - cd)^2$ 45. $(ab + cd)^2$

46. $a(ax - 1)^2$ 47. $(a - b)[(a - b)^2 + 4]$

48. $(ax + 3by)^2$ 49. $(3ax - by)^2$

50. (a)

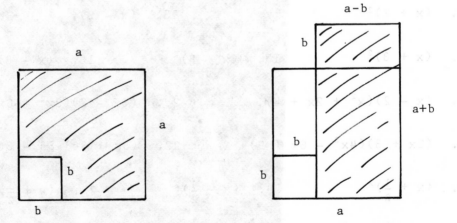

The two shaded regions have equal area. The area on the
left is $a^2 - b^2$. The area on the right is $(a + b)(a - b)$.

(b)

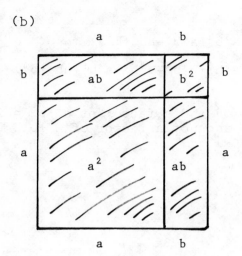

The area of the total square is $(a + b)^2$. The area of this same square is the sum of the areas of the sub-regions: $a^2 + 2ab + b^2$.

(c)

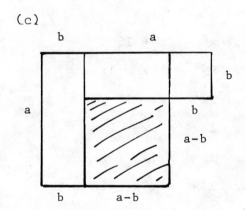

The area of the shaded square is $(a - b)^2$. This same square can be obtained from a configuration of area $a^2 + b^2$ (the sum of two squares: one of side a, the other of side b) by removing two rectangles each of area ab. The area of the shaded square is thus also $a^2 + b^2 - 2ab = a^2 - 2ab + b^2$.

52. (a) routine

(b) $a^5 - b^5 = (a-b)(a^4 + a^3b + a^2b^2 + ab^3 + b^4)$

(c) $a^6 - b^6 = (a-b)(a^5 + a^4b + a^3b^2 + a^2b^3 + ab^4 + b^5)$

53. $a^n - b^n = (a-b)(a^{n-1} + a^{n-2}b + a^{n-3}b^2 + \cdots + a^2b^{n-3} + ab^{n-2} + b^{n-1})$

54. (a) routine

    (b) $a^7+b^7 = (a+b)(a^6-a^5b+a^4b^2-a^3b^3+a^2b^4-ab^5+b^6)$

    (c) $a^9+b^9 = (a+b)(a^8-a^7b+a^6b^2-a^5b^3+a^4b^4-a^3b^5+a^2b^6-ab^7+b^8)$

55. $a+b = 5$ is a factor of $a^3+b^3 = 35$ and a factor of $a^5+b^5 = 275$ but not a factor of $a^4+b^4 = 97$ and not a factor of $a^6+b^6 = 793$.

SECTION 1.7

1. $x^2 + 5x + 4$

2. $x^2 - 3x - 4$

3. $x^2 + 3x - 4$

4. $x^2 - 5x + 4$

5. $x^2 + 8x + 15$

6. $x^2 - 8x + 15$

7. $x^2 - 2x - 15$

8. $6x^2 + 19x + 15$

9. $6x^2 - x - 15$

10. $6x^2 + x - 15$

11. $6x^2 - 19x + 15$

12. $12x^2 + 5x - 2$

13. $12x^2 - 5x - 2$

14. $12x^2 + 11x + 2$

15. $12x^2 - 11x + 2$

16. $18x^2 + 27x - 5$

17. $6x^2 - 13x + 6$

18. $6x^2 - 5x - 6$

19. $5x^2 - 7x + 2$

20. $5x^2 + 3x - 2$

21. $10x^2 + 33x - 7$

22. $7x^2 + 3x - 22$

23. $7x^2 - 79x + 22$

24. $11x^2 + 79x + 14$

25. $x^4 + 7x^2 + 10$

26. $x^4 + x^2 - 42$

27. $5x^4 + 7x^2 + 2$

28. $14x^4 - 33x^2 - 5$

29. $2A^6 + 5A^3 - 12$

30. $5A^6 + 39A^3 - 8$

31. $24A^4B^4 - 10A^2B^2 - 25$

32. $18A^2B^4 - 43AB^2 - 70$

SECTION 1.8

1. $(x + 3)(x + 1)$ 2. $(x - 1)(x - 3)$ 3. $(x + 3)(x - 1)$

4. $(x + 4)(x + 2)$ 5. $(x + 3)(x + 5)$ 6. $(x - 5)(x - 3)$

7. $(x - 2)(x + 1)$ 8. $(x - 5)(x - 1)$ 9. $(x - 9)(x - 3)$

10. $(x - 5)(x - 7)$ 11. $(x + 40)(x + 10)$ 12. $(x - 2)(x - 10)$

13. $(x + 7)(x - 4)$ 14. $(x + 3)(x - 2)$ 15. $(x - 12)(x + 2)$

16. $(x - 2)(5x + 3)$ 17. $(x + 2)(5x - 3)$ 18. $(8x + 3)(2x + 3)$

19. $(2x + 1)(x + 2)$ 20. $(2x + 1)(x - 2)$ 21. $(2x + 3)(x - 1)$

22. $(3x + 2)(2x + 5)$ 23. $(3x + 2)(2x - 5)$ 24. $(2x + 3)(x + 10)$

25. $(25x + 3)(x + 2)$ 26. $(6x + 1)(2x - 3)$ 27. $(2x - 5)(x - 10)$

28. $(4x - 1)(3x - 2)$ 29. $(2x + 5)(2x + 5)$ 30. $(4x + 1)(4x + 5)$

31. $(6x - 1)(6x - 1)$ 32. $(3x + 4)(4x - 1)$ 33. $(5x + 2)(3x - 4)$

34. $(x + A)(x + B)$ 35. $(x - A)(x - B)$ 36. $(x + A)(x - B)$

37. $(x - A)(x + B)$

38. $x^2 + 2x + 1 - A = (x + 1)^2 - A^2 = (x + 1 + A)(x + 1 - A)$

39. $x^2 - 2x + 1 - A^2 = (x - 1)^2 - A^2 = (x - 1 + A)(x - 1 - A)$

40. $(x + \frac{1}{2})(x - 2)$ 41. $(x + \frac{1}{2})(x + 2)$ 42. $(2x + \frac{1}{3})(3x + \frac{1}{2})$

43. $(2x - \frac{1}{2})(3x + \frac{1}{3})$ 44. $(rx - s)(tx - u)$

45. If

$$x^2 + 1 = (ax + b)(cx + d),$$

then $x^2 + 1$ has to be zero at $x = -b/a$ and at $x = -d/c$. This is impossible: since x^2 is nonnegative, $x^2 + 1$ cannot take on any value less than 1.

SECTION 1.9

1. $x(x + 1)(x - 1)$ 2. $2x(5 + x)(5 - x)$

3. $x^2(x - 5)(x - 1)$ 4. $(x^4 + 1)(x^2 + 1)(x + 1)(x - 1)$

5. $3x^3(x - 7)(x - 5)$ 6. $16(x + y)^2(x - y)^2$

7. $x(x + 3)(x - 2)$ 8. $3x^2(x - 3)^2$

9. $x(2x - 1)(x + 2)$ 10. $-2(x - 1)$

11. $(x^2 + 2)(x + 2)(x - 2)$ 12. $x^3(2x - 1)(5x + 2)$

13. $x^3 - x^2 - x + 1 = (x^3 - x) - (x^2 - 1) = x(x^2 - 1) - (x^2 - 1)$
$$= (x^2 - 1)(x - 1)$$
$$= (x + 1)(x - 1)^2$$

14. $x(x^2 + 1)(x^2 + 3)$

15. $3x^4 - 24x^2 + 48 = 3(x^4 - 8x^2 + 16) = 3(x^2 - 4)^2$
$$= 3(x + 2)^2(x - 2)^2$$

16. $2x^3(3x - 5)(x + 1)$

17. $r^2 - a^2 - 2ac - c^2 = r^2 - (a^2 + 2ac + c^2)$
$$= r^2 - (a + c)^2$$
$$= (r + a + c)(r - a - c)$$

18. $(a - b)^3 - 4(a - b) = (a - b)[(a - b)^2 - 4]$
$$= (a - b)(a - b + 2)(a - b - 2)$$

19. $[3(a - b) + 4][(a - b) + 2] = (3a - 3b + 4)(a - b + 2)$

20. $3a^2r^2(r + a)(r - a)$

21. $x^4 - (x - 1)^4 = [x^2 + (x - 1)^2] \, [x^2 - (x - 1)^2]$

$$= [x^2 + (x - 1)^2] \, [x + (x - 1)] \, [x - (x - 1)]$$

$$= [x^2 + (x - 1)^2] \, (2x - 1)$$

22. $(x + a)(x - a)(x + 2a)(x - 2a)$

23. $(x + a)(x - a)(x^2 + ax + a^2)(x^2 - ax + a^2)$

24. $(x + c)^3 - (x^3 + c^3) = (x+c)(x+c)^2 - (x+c)(x^2-cx+c^2)$

$$= (x+c)(x^2+2cx+c^2) - (x+c)(x^2-cx+c^2)$$

$$= (x+c)(x^2+2cx+c^2-x^2+cx-c^2)$$

$$= 3cx(x+c)$$

25. $(x + 2)^2 - (x^2 - 4)^2 = (x + 2 + x^2 - 4)(x + 2 - x^2 + 4)$

$$= -(x^2 + x - 2)(x^2 - x - 6)$$

$$= -(x + 2)(x - 1)(x - 3)(x + 2)$$

$$= -(x + 2)^2(x - 1)(x - 3)$$

26. $64x^2 - (x^2 + 16)^2 = (8x + x^2 + 16)(8x - x^2 - 16)$

$$= -(x^2 + 8x + 16)(x^2 - 8x + 16)$$

$$= -(x + 4)^2(x - 4)^2$$

27. $x^3 + x^2 + (12x - 45)(x + 1) = x^2(x + 1) + (12x - 45)(x + 1)$

$$= (x + 1)(x^2 + 12x - 45)$$

$$= (x + 1)(x + 15)(x - 3)$$

28. $6(x - y) - 10(x^2 - y^2) = 2(x - y)[3 - 5(x + y)]$
$$= 2(x - y)(3 - 5x - 5y)$$

29. $x^2 + 9y^2 + 6xy - 1 = (x^2 + 6xy + 9y^2) - 1$
$$= (x + 3y)^2 - 1$$
$$= (x + 3y + 1)(x + 3y - 1)$$

30. $x^3 - c^2 + 2cx - c^3 - x^2 = x^3 - c^3 - (x^2 - 2cx + c^2)$
$$= (x^3 - c^3) - (x - c)^2$$
$$= (x - c)(x^2 + cx + c^2) - (x - c)^2$$
$$= (x - c)(x^2 + cx + c^2 - x + c)$$
$$= (x - c)[x^2 + (c - 1)x + c^2 + c]$$

31. $12 - 5(2x-1) - 3(2x-1)^2 = -[3(2x-1)^2 + 5(2x-1) - 12]$
$$= -[3(2x-1) - 4][(2x-1) + 3]$$
$$= -(6x - 3 - 4)(2x - 1 + 3)$$
$$= -2(6x - 7)(x + 1)$$

32. $(x^2+y^2)^2 + x^2y^2 + 3x^4 - 2y^4 = (x^2+y^2)^2 + (3x^4+x^2y^2-2y^4)$
$$= (x^2+y^2)^2 + (3x^2-2y^2)(x^2+y^2)$$
$$= (x^2+y^2)(x^2+y^2+3x^2-2y^2)$$
$$= (x^2+y^2)(4x^2-y^2)$$
$$= (x^2+y^2)(2x+y)(2x-y)$$

SECTION 1.10

1. $\dfrac{1 + 2x}{x^2 - 1}$ 2. $\dfrac{x + 5}{2x^3}$ 3. $\dfrac{10x}{2x^2 + 1}$

4. $\dfrac{1}{x^2 - 1}$ 5. $\dfrac{x - 2}{2}$ 6. $\dfrac{4x^2}{x^2 + 2}$

7. $\dfrac{x^2 + 4}{x - 1}$ 8. $-\dfrac{2^n}{x^n}$ 9. $\dfrac{x + 3}{x - 5}$

10. $\dfrac{x + 2}{2x - 1}$ 11. 5   12. 1

13. $2x^2 + 3x + 2$ 14. $2x + 3$ 15. $2x^2 - 2x - 5$

16. $x^3 + x + 2$ 17. $x^3 - 2x + 3$ 18. $2x^2 - 6x + 6$

19. $4x^2 + 15x - 10$ 20. $2x^4 + 10x^2 + 14$

21. $\dfrac{1}{6x^2}$ for $x \neq 0$ 22. $\dfrac{3}{2}$ for $x \neq 0$

23. $\dfrac{2x}{x^2 + 1}$ for all real x 24. $\dfrac{x(x^2 + 1)}{8}$ for all real x

25. $\dfrac{1}{x^6}$ for $x \neq 0$ 26. $\dfrac{4x^2}{x^2 + 1}$ for all real x

27. $\dfrac{4}{x - 1}$ for $x \neq 1$

28. $\dfrac{2}{3}$ for $x \neq 0$

29. $\dfrac{1}{x(x + 1)}$ for $x \neq -1, 0, 1$

30. 4 for $x \neq 0$

31. $2\left(x^2 + \dfrac{1}{x^2}\right)$ for $x \neq 0$

32. $\dfrac{x^5}{x^2 - 1}$ for $x \neq -1, 0, 1$

33. $\dfrac{a - x}{a^2 + x^2}$ for $x \neq -a$

34. $-\dfrac{1}{x}$ for $x \neq 0, -1$

35. $\dfrac{2x - 4}{x + 2}$ for $x \neq 0, -2$

36. $\left(\dfrac{a}{x} + \dfrac{b}{y}\right)\left(\dfrac{a}{x} - \dfrac{b}{y}\right)$

37. $\left(1 - \dfrac{x}{y}\right)\left(1 + \dfrac{x}{y} + \dfrac{x^2}{y^2}\right)$

38. $\left(4 + \dfrac{a^2}{x^2}\right)\left(2 + \dfrac{a}{x}\right)\left(2 - \dfrac{a}{x}\right)$

39. (a), (c), (e), (f) follow as can be verified by cross-multiplication and the fact that $ad = bc$;

(b) does not follow:

$$\dfrac{2}{3} = \dfrac{4}{6} \quad \text{but} \quad \dfrac{2}{6} \neq \dfrac{3}{4} \; ;$$

(d) does not follow:

$$\dfrac{2}{3} = \dfrac{4}{6} \quad \text{but} \quad \dfrac{2 + 3}{2 - 3} \neq \dfrac{4 - 6}{4 + 6} \, .$$

SECTION 1.11

1. $x - 5 + \dfrac{15}{x + 5}$

2. $x^3 + 3$

3. $2x^2 + 10x + 50 + \dfrac{400}{x - 5}$

4. $x^2 + 3x + 3$

5. $x^2 + 2x + 4$

6. $4x^2 - 6x + 9$

7. $a^2 + ab + b^2$

8. $a + b$

9. $x^4 - x^2 + 1 - \dfrac{1}{x^2 + 1}$

10. $x^5 + 1$

11. $a^6 + a^5b + a^4b^2 + a^3b^3 + a^2b^4 + ab^5 + b^6$

12. $x^3 - 1$

13. $x^2 + 4 + \dfrac{9}{x^2 - 2}$

14. $x^3 + 2x^2 + 3x + 4$

15. $x^3 - 3x + 1$

16. $x^2 + 2x + 4 + \dfrac{6x + 1}{x^2 - 2x}$

17. $x^2 - 4 - \dfrac{x^2 - 6x - 5}{2x^3 + x + 1}$

18. $3x^2 - \dfrac{3}{2}x - \dfrac{3}{4} + \dfrac{17x+4}{8x^2+4x+4}$

19. $(x+4)(x-3)(x+2)(x-1)$

20. $20(x-1)^2(x-3)(x+2)$

21. $(x - a)^2(x - b)$

22. $(2x^2 + 1)(x - 2)(x - 1)$

23. $(x+a)^2(x-a)(x^2+ax+a^2)$

24. $(x^2 + a^2)(x - a)(x + a)^4$

SECTION 1.12

1. (b): $3.1416 = \dfrac{31416}{10000}$ and (c): $(1+ \sqrt{2})(1- \sqrt{2}) = (1)^2 - (\sqrt{2})^2$
$$= -1$$

2. (a) $2 \cdot 10^2 + 4 \cdot 10 + 7$ (b) $4 \cdot 10 + 9$

    (c) $5 \cdot 10^3 + 7 \cdot 10^2 + 8 \cdot 10 + 3$

    (d) $1 \cdot 10^4 + 6 \cdot 10^3 + 0 \cdot 10^2 + 4 \cdot 10 + 8$

3. $x^4 - y^4$ 4. $x^3 - (3+a)x^2 + (1+3a)x - a$

5. $2x^4 + x^3 - 4x^2 + 11x - 4$ 6. $x^4 - 2x^2y^2 + y^4$

7. $x^4 - x^3y + xy^3 - y^4$ 8. $x^4 - ax^3 - 3a^2x^2 + 5a^3x - 2a^4$

9. $(3x + 10)(3x - 10)$ 10. $(x + \sqrt{5})(x - \sqrt{5})$

11. $(3x + 2)(9x^2 - 6x + 4)$ 12. $(x + 7)(x + 1)$

13. $(5x + 7)(x + 1)$ 14. $(2x - 3)(x + 3)$

15. $2a(3x^2 + 4)$ 16. $(a^2x^2 + b^2)(ax + b)(ax - b)$

17. $2x(4x + 5)(2x - 1)$

18. $a^4b^6x^6 - a^4 = a^4(b^6x^6 - 1)$
$$= a^4(b^3x^3 + 1)(b^3x^3 - 1)$$
$$= a^4(bx+1)(bx-1)(b^2x^2 + bx +1)(b^2x^2 - bx +1)$$

19. $(3x - 2)(x + 2)$

20. $2x^3 - x + 2a^3 - a = 2x^3 + 2a^3 - x - a$

$$= 2(x^3 + a^3) - (x + a)$$

$$= 2(x + a)(x^2 - ax + a^2) - (x + a)$$

$$= (x + a)(2x^2 - 2ax + 2a^2 - 1)$$

21. $(x - r)(x - 1)$

22. $(x + 1)(x - r)$

23. $(x + r)(x - 1)$

24. $\left(\dfrac{a}{b} + \dfrac{c}{d}\right)\left(\dfrac{a}{b} - \dfrac{c}{d}\right)$

25. $\left(\dfrac{a}{x} - \dfrac{b}{y}\right)\left(\dfrac{a^2}{x^2} + \dfrac{ab}{xy} + \dfrac{b^2}{y^2}\right)$

26. $\dfrac{1}{a^2}(x + \tfrac{3}{2})(x - 1)$

27. $x - 4$

28. $x^2 - 2ax + a^2$

29. $x + 2$

30. $2(x^2 - ax + a^2)$

31. $1 - 5x$

32. $(c - a)x + (d - b)$

33. $5x^3 + 4x^2 + x + 1$

34. 2

35. $\dfrac{a - x}{a + x}$

36. $\dfrac{a^2 + x^2}{a^2 - x^2}$

37. $\dfrac{a^3 - x^3}{a^3 + x^3}$

38. $2x + h$

39. $-\dfrac{1}{x(x + h)}$

40. $-\dfrac{2x + h}{x^2(x + h)^2}$

41. $x^2 - 3x + 5$

42. $2x + 1$

43. $x^3 - x + \dfrac{x}{x^2 + 1}$

44. $(3x^2 + 1)(x+2)(x^2 - 2x + 4)$

45. $(x+2)(x+5)(x+6)(x+1)$

46. $(x + \frac{1}{3})(x + \frac{2}{3})^2$

47. If p is odd, then p is of the form 2n+1 with n an integer. Therefore

$$p^2 = (2n + 1)^2 = 4n^2 + 4n + 1 = 2(2n^2 + 2n) + 1.$$

Setting

$$2n^2 + 2n = q$$

we have

$$p^2 = 2q + 1.$$

This shows that p^2 is odd. □

48. If p is not divisible by 3, then p is of the form 3n+1 or 3n+2. In the first case

$$p^2 = (3n + 1)^2 = 9n^2 + 6n + 1 = 3(3n^2 + 2n) + 1,$$

and in the second

$$p^2 = (3n + 2)^2 = 9n^2 + 12n + 4 = 3(3n^2 + 4n + 1) + 1.$$

In both cases p^2 is of the form 3q+1 and thus not divisible by 3. □

49. $(a^2 + b^2)(c^2 + d^2) = (ac + bd)^2 + (bc - ad)^2$:

$$
\begin{aligned}
(a^2 + b^2)(c^2 + d^2) &= a^2c^2 + a^2d^2 + b^2c^2 + b^2d^2 \\
&= a^2c^2 + b^2d^2 + b^2c^2 + a^2d^2 \\
&= (a^2c^2 + 2acbd + b^2d^2) \\
&\quad + (b^2c^2 - 2acbd + a^2d^2) \\
&= (ac + bd)^2 + (bc - ad)^2. \;\square
\end{aligned}
$$

50. $\dfrac{R_1 R_2}{R_1 + R_2}$

51. $(R_1 \oplus R_2) \oplus R_3 = \dfrac{1}{\dfrac{1}{R_1 \oplus R_2} + \dfrac{1}{R_3}} = \dfrac{1}{\left(\dfrac{1}{R_1} + \dfrac{1}{R_2}\right) + \dfrac{1}{R_3}}$

$R_1 \oplus (R_2 \oplus R_3) = \dfrac{1}{\dfrac{1}{R_1} + \dfrac{1}{R_2 \oplus R_3}} = \dfrac{1}{\dfrac{1}{R_1} + \left(\dfrac{1}{R_2} + \dfrac{1}{R_3}\right)}$

$(R_1 \oplus R_2) \oplus R_3 = R_1 \oplus (R_2 \oplus R_3)$ because

$$\left(\dfrac{1}{R_1} + \dfrac{1}{R_2}\right) + \dfrac{1}{R_3} = \dfrac{1}{R_1} + \left(\dfrac{1}{R_2} + \dfrac{1}{R_3}\right).$$

52. (a) $\frac{1}{2}R_1$ (b) $\frac{1}{5}R_1$ (c) $\left(\dfrac{\alpha\beta}{\alpha+\beta}\right)R_1$ (d) $\frac{1}{3}R_1$

   (e) $\frac{1}{9}R_1$ (f) $\dfrac{R_1}{n}$ (g) $\dfrac{2R_1}{n(n+1)}$

53. (a) $\dfrac{RR_1}{R_1 - R}$ (b) $\left(\dfrac{\alpha}{1 - \alpha}\right)R_1$

54. (a) $\frac{19}{12}R_0$ (b) $\frac{3}{19}R_0$ 55. $\frac{3}{20}R_0$

56. the effective resistance is reduced by $\dfrac{R_0^2}{2R_1}$:

$$R_1 \oplus R_1 = \frac{R_1}{2},$$

$$(R_1 + R_0) \oplus (R_1 - R_0) = \cfrac{1}{\cfrac{1}{R_1 + R_0} + \cfrac{1}{R_1 - R_0}}$$

$$= \cfrac{1}{\cfrac{2R_1}{R_1^2 - R_0^2}} = \frac{R_1^2 - R_0^2}{2R_1} = \frac{R_1}{2} - \frac{R_0^2}{2R_1}$$

57. (a) $12 + (10 \oplus 8 \oplus 5) + (4 \oplus 4) = 16\frac{6}{17}$ ohms

(b) $12 + \{10 \oplus [5 + (4 \oplus 4)]\} + 20 = 36\frac{2}{17}$ ohms

58. The cross ratio can be 0 only if $x_1 = x_2$ or $x_3 = x_4$. This cannot happen since by assumption all the x's are distinct.
    As we show below, a cross ratio cannot be 1 because the assumption that it is 1 leads to the conclusion that $x_4 = x_2$, again violating the assumption that all the x's are distinct:

$$\frac{(x_1 - x_2)(x_3 - x_4)}{(x_2 - x_3)(x_4 - x_1)} = 1 \qquad \text{implies}$$

$$(x_1 - x_2)(x_3 - x_4) = (x_2 - x_3)(x_4 - x_1)$$

$$\cancel{x_1 x_3} - x_1 x_4 - x_2 x_3 + \cancel{x_2 x_4} = \cancel{x_2 x_4} - x_2 x_1 - x_3 x_4 + \cancel{x_3 x_1}$$

$$-x_1 x_4 - x_2 x_3 = -x_1 x_2 - x_3 x_4$$

$$x_3 x_4 - x_1 x_4 = x_2 x_3 - x_1 x_2$$

$$(x_3 - x_1)x_4 = x_2(x_3 - x_1)$$

$$x_4 = x_2. \qquad (\text{since } x_3 - x_1 \neq 0)$$

59. $[0,1,2,3] \neq [1,0,2,3]$ since

$$[0,1,2,3] = \frac{(0-1)(2-3)}{(1-2)(3-0)} = \frac{1}{-3} = -\frac{1}{3},$$

$$[1,0,2,3] = \frac{(1-0)(2-3)}{(0-2)(3-1)} = \frac{-1}{-4} = \frac{1}{4}.$$

60. There are 4 possibilities for the first slot, leaving 3 possibilities for the second slot, 2 possibilities for the third slot, 1 possibility for the fourth slot. The number of possible orderings is therefore

$$4 \times 3 \times 2 \times 1 = 24.$$

61. In expanded form we have

$$[x_1, x_2, x_3, x_4] = \frac{(x_1 - x_2)(x_3 - x_4)}{(x_2 - x_3)(x_4 - x_1)},$$

$$[x_4, x_3, x_2, x_1] = \frac{(x_4 - x_3)(x_2 - x_1)}{(x_3 - x_2)(x_1 - x_4)},$$

$$[x_2, x_1, x_4, x_3] = \frac{(x_2 - x_1)(x_4 - x_3)}{(x_1 - x_4)(x_3 - x_2)},$$

$$[x_3, x_4, x_1, x_2] = \frac{(x_3 - x_4)(x_1 - x_2)}{(x_4 - x_1)(x_2 - x_3)}.$$ The four quotients are clearly all equal.

62. (a) $[x_1, x_4, x_3, x_2] = \frac{1}{x}$:

$$[x_1, x_4, x_3, x_2] = \frac{(x_1 - x_4)(x_3 - x_2)}{(x_4 - x_3)(x_2 - x_1)} = \frac{(x_2 - x_3)(x_4 - x_1)}{(x_1 - x_2)(x_3 - x_4)} = \frac{1}{x}$$

(b) $[x_2, x_3, x_4, x_1]$, $\quad [x_4, x_1, x_2, x_3]$, $\quad [x_3, x_2, x_1, x_4]$

63. (a) $[x_1, x_3, x_2, x_4] = \dfrac{(x_1 - x_3)(x_2 - x_4)}{(x_3 - x_2)(x_4 - x_1)}$,

$$1 - x = 1 - \frac{(x_1 - x_2)(x_3 - x_4)}{(x_2 - x_3)(x_4 - x_1)}$$

$$= \frac{(x_2 - x_3)(x_4 - x_1) - (x_1 - x_2)(x_3 - x_4)}{(x_2 - x_3)(x_4 - x_1)}$$

$$= \frac{x_2 x_4 - x_1 x_2 - x_3 x_4 + x_1 x_3 - x_1 x_3 + x_1 x_4 + x_2 x_3 - x_2 x_4}{(x_2 - x_3)(x_4 - x_1)}$$

$$= \frac{x_1 x_2 + x_3 x_4 - x_1 x_4 - x_2 x_3}{(x_3 - x_2)(x_4 - x_1)}$$

$$= \frac{x_1 x_2 - x_1 x_4 + x_3 x_4 - x_2 x_3}{(x_3 - x_2)(x_4 - x_1)}$$

$$= \frac{x_1 (x_2 - x_4) - x_3 (x_2 - x_4)}{(x_3 - x_2)(x_4 - x_1)}$$

$$= \frac{(x_1 - x_3)(x_2 - x_4)}{(x_3 - x_2)(x_4 - x_1)} = [x_1, x_3, x_2, x_4] .$$

(b) $[x_4, x_2, x_3, x_1]$, $[x_3, x_1, x_4, x_2]$, $.[x_2, x_4, x_1, x_3]$

64. $[x_1, x_4, x_2, x_3]$, $[x_4, x_1, x_3, x_2]$, $[x_3, x_2, x_4, x_1]$, $[x_2, x_3, x_1, x_4]$

These are the orderings of Exercise 63 with the second and fourth entries interchanged.

65. $[x_1, x_3, x_4, x_2]$, $[x_2, x_4, x_3, x_1]$, $[x_4, x_2, x_1, x_3]$, $[x_3, x_1, x_2, x_4]$

These are the orderings of Exercise 62 with the second and third entries interchanged.

66. $[x_1, x_2, x_4, x_3]$, $[x_2, x_1, x_3, x_4]$, $[x_4, x_3, x_1, x_2]$, $[x_3, x_4, x_2, x_1]$

These are the orderings of Exercise 65 with the second and fourth entries interchanged.

67. $x = -1$ in which case the only possible values for the cross ratio are $-1, 2, \frac{1}{2}$.

SECTION 2.1

1. $\sqrt{50} = \sqrt{(25)(2)} = 5\sqrt{2} \cong 5(1.414) = 7.070$

2. $\sqrt{44} = \sqrt{(4)(11)} = 2\sqrt{11} \cong 2(3.317) = 6.634$

3. $\sqrt{180} = \sqrt{(36)(5)} = 6\sqrt{5} \cong 6(2.236) = 13.416$

4. $\sqrt{7500} = \sqrt{(2500)(3)} = 50\sqrt{3} \cong 50(1.732) = 86.60$

5. $\sqrt{0.5} = \sqrt{\frac{1}{2}} = \frac{1}{2}\sqrt{2} \cong \frac{1}{2}(1.414) = 0.707$

6. $\sqrt{0.76} = \sqrt{\frac{76}{100}} = \frac{2}{10}\sqrt{19} \cong \frac{1}{5}(4.359) \cong 0.872$

7. $\sqrt{0.0019} = \sqrt{\frac{19}{10000}} = \frac{1}{100}\sqrt{19} \cong \frac{1}{100}(4.359) \cong 0.044$

8. $\sqrt{1.12} = \sqrt{\frac{112}{100}} = \frac{4}{10}\sqrt{7} \cong \frac{2}{5}(2.646) \cong 1.058$

9. $\sqrt{\frac{3}{4}} = \frac{1}{2}\sqrt{3} \cong \frac{1}{2}(1.732) = 0.866$

10. $\sqrt{\frac{5}{36}} = \frac{1}{6}\sqrt{5} \cong \frac{1}{6}(2.236) \cong 0.373$

11. $\sqrt{\frac{24}{49}} = \frac{2}{7}\sqrt{6} \cong \frac{2}{7}(2.449) \cong 0.700$

12. 0.6

13. $\dfrac{1}{\sqrt{2}} = \dfrac{1}{\sqrt{2}} \cdot \dfrac{\sqrt{2}}{\sqrt{2}} = \frac{1}{2}\sqrt{2}$
          14. $\dfrac{1}{\sqrt{5}} = \dfrac{1}{\sqrt{5}} \cdot \dfrac{\sqrt{5}}{\sqrt{5}} = \frac{1}{5}\sqrt{5}$

15. $\dfrac{3\sqrt{2}}{\sqrt{6}} = \dfrac{3\sqrt{2}}{\sqrt{3}\sqrt{2}} = \sqrt{3}$
          16. $\dfrac{\sqrt{3}}{\sqrt{15}} = \dfrac{\sqrt{3}}{\sqrt{5}\sqrt{3}} = \dfrac{1}{\sqrt{5}} = \frac{1}{5}\sqrt{5}$

17. $\dfrac{1}{1 + \sqrt{6}} = \dfrac{1}{1 + \sqrt{6}} \cdot \dfrac{1 - \sqrt{6}}{1 - \sqrt{6}} = \dfrac{1 - \sqrt{6}}{-5} = \frac{1}{5}(\sqrt{6} - 1)$

18. $\dfrac{\sqrt{7}}{2 - \sqrt{7}} = \dfrac{\sqrt{7}}{2 - \sqrt{7}} \cdot \dfrac{2 + \sqrt{7}}{2 + \sqrt{7}} = \dfrac{2\sqrt{7} + 7}{-3} = -\dfrac{2\sqrt{7} + 7}{3}$

19. $\dfrac{1}{\sqrt{11} - \sqrt{10}} = \dfrac{1}{\sqrt{11} - \sqrt{10}} \cdot \dfrac{\sqrt{11} + \sqrt{10}}{\sqrt{11} + \sqrt{10}} = \dfrac{\sqrt{11} + \sqrt{10}}{1} = \sqrt{11} + \sqrt{10}$

20. $\dfrac{\sqrt{3}}{\sqrt{5} + \sqrt{3}} = \dfrac{\sqrt{3}}{\sqrt{5} + \sqrt{3}} \cdot \dfrac{\sqrt{5} - \sqrt{3}}{\sqrt{5} - \sqrt{3}} = \dfrac{\sqrt{15} - 3}{2}$

21. $\dfrac{\sqrt{5}}{\sqrt{5} - \sqrt{3}} = \dfrac{\sqrt{5}}{\sqrt{5} - \sqrt{3}} \cdot \dfrac{\sqrt{5} + \sqrt{3}}{\sqrt{5} + \sqrt{3}} = \dfrac{5 + \sqrt{15}}{2}$

22. $\dfrac{\sqrt{5} + \sqrt{2}}{\sqrt{5} - \sqrt{2}} = \dfrac{\sqrt{5} + \sqrt{2}}{\sqrt{5} - \sqrt{2}} \cdot \dfrac{\sqrt{5} + \sqrt{2}}{\sqrt{5} + \sqrt{2}} = \dfrac{7 + 2\sqrt{10}}{3}$

23. $\dfrac{12\sqrt{7}}{\sqrt{14} - \sqrt{2}} = \dfrac{12\sqrt{7}}{\sqrt{14} - \sqrt{2}} \cdot \dfrac{\sqrt{14} + \sqrt{2}}{\sqrt{14} + \sqrt{2}} = \dfrac{84\sqrt{2} + 12\sqrt{14}}{12} = 7\sqrt{2} + \sqrt{14}$

24. $\dfrac{6\sqrt{24}}{3 - \sqrt{3}} = \dfrac{(6)(2\sqrt{6})}{3 - \sqrt{3}} \cdot \dfrac{3 + \sqrt{3}}{3 + \sqrt{3}} = \dfrac{12\sqrt{6}(3 + \sqrt{3})}{6}$

$$= \dfrac{2\sqrt{6}(3 + \sqrt{3})}{3}$$

$$= \dfrac{6\sqrt{6} + 2\sqrt{18}}{3}$$

$$= \dfrac{6\sqrt{6} + 6\sqrt{2}}{3} = 2\sqrt{6} + 2\sqrt{2}$$

25. $\dfrac{x - y}{\sqrt{x} - \sqrt{y}} = \dfrac{(\sqrt{x} + \sqrt{y})(\sqrt{x} - \sqrt{y})}{\sqrt{x} - \sqrt{y}} = \sqrt{x} + \sqrt{y}$

26. $\dfrac{x^2 - y^2}{\sqrt{x} - \sqrt{y}} = \dfrac{x^2 - y^2}{\sqrt{x} - \sqrt{y}} \cdot \dfrac{\sqrt{x} + \sqrt{y}}{\sqrt{x} + \sqrt{y}} = \dfrac{(x^2 - y^2)(\sqrt{x} + \sqrt{y})}{x - y}$

$$= (x + y)(\sqrt{x} + \sqrt{y})$$

27. $\dfrac{(x - y)^3}{\sqrt{x} - \sqrt{y}} = \dfrac{(x - y)^3}{\sqrt{x} - \sqrt{y}} \cdot \dfrac{\sqrt{x} + \sqrt{y}}{\sqrt{x} + \sqrt{y}} = \dfrac{(x - y)^3(\sqrt{x} + \sqrt{y})}{x - y}$

$$= (x - y)^2(\sqrt{x} + \sqrt{y})$$

28. $\dfrac{x - 2\sqrt{a}\sqrt{x} + a}{\sqrt{x} - \sqrt{a}} = \dfrac{(\sqrt{x} - \sqrt{a})^2}{\sqrt{x} - \sqrt{a}} = \sqrt{x} - \sqrt{a}$

29. $\dfrac{h}{\sqrt{x + h} - \sqrt{x}} = \dfrac{h}{\sqrt{x + h} - \sqrt{x}} \cdot \dfrac{\sqrt{x + h} + \sqrt{x}}{\sqrt{x + h} + \sqrt{x}} = \dfrac{h(\sqrt{x + h} + \sqrt{x})}{h}$

$$= \sqrt{x + h} + \sqrt{x}$$

30.
$$\frac{2h}{\sqrt{x-h} - \sqrt{x+h}} = \frac{2h}{\sqrt{x-h} - \sqrt{x+h}} \cdot \frac{\sqrt{x-h} + \sqrt{x+h}}{\sqrt{x-h} + \sqrt{x+h}}$$

$$= \frac{2h(\sqrt{x-h} + \sqrt{x+h})}{-2h} = -\sqrt{x-h} - \sqrt{x+h}$$

31. $\sqrt{\dfrac{3}{5}} + \sqrt{\dfrac{5}{3}} = \dfrac{1}{5}\sqrt{15} + \dfrac{1}{3}\sqrt{15} = (\dfrac{1}{5} + \dfrac{1}{3})\sqrt{15} = \dfrac{8}{15}\sqrt{15}$

32. $\sqrt{\dfrac{9}{5}} - \sqrt{\dfrac{5}{4}} = \dfrac{3}{5}\sqrt{5} - \dfrac{1}{2}\sqrt{5} = (\dfrac{3}{5} - \dfrac{1}{2})\sqrt{5} = \dfrac{1}{10}\sqrt{5}$

33. $\sqrt{\dfrac{m}{n}} + \sqrt{\dfrac{n}{m}} = \dfrac{1}{n}\sqrt{mn} + \dfrac{1}{m}\sqrt{mn} = (\dfrac{1}{n} + \dfrac{1}{m})\sqrt{mn} = (\dfrac{m+n}{mn})\sqrt{mn}$

34. 1.999396 is closer to 2 than is 2.002225

35. (a) F is doubled (b) F is divided by 4 (c) $r = \sqrt{G\dfrac{M_1 M_2}{F}}$

36. Only if $x \geq 0$. If $x < 0$, then $\sqrt{x^2} = -x$. For example,
$$\sqrt{(-1)^2} = \sqrt{1} = 1 = -(-1).$$

37. $(\sqrt{x})^n \geq 0$ and its square is x^n :
$$(\sqrt{x})^n \cdot (\sqrt{x})^n = (\sqrt{x} \cdot \sqrt{x})^n = x^n.$$
by (1.4.1)__|

38. (a) $\dfrac{\sqrt{1.6} - \sqrt{1}}{0.6} = \dfrac{10}{6}(\dfrac{2}{5}\sqrt{10} - 1) = \dfrac{2}{3}\sqrt{10} - \dfrac{5}{3} \cong \dfrac{2}{3}(3.162) - \dfrac{5}{3} \cong 0.441$

(b) $\dfrac{\sqrt{1.1} - \sqrt{1}}{0.1} = 10(\dfrac{1}{10}\sqrt{11}\sqrt{10} - 1) = \sqrt{11}\sqrt{10} - 10$

$$\cong (3.317)(3.162) - 10 \cong 0.488$$

39. (a) $\sqrt{2}$ s (b) $\sqrt{3}$ s   40. $\sqrt{w^2 + \ell^2 + h^2}$

41. n = 4:

$$(n\sqrt{3})^2 + [(n + 1)\sqrt{2}]^2 = (n\sqrt{5})^2 + [(n - 1)\sqrt{2}]^2 \quad \text{gives}$$

$$3n^2 + 2(n + 1)^2 = 5n^2 + 2(n - 1)^2$$

$$2[(n + 1)^2 - (n - 1)^2] = 2n^2$$

$$(n + 1 + n - 1)(n + 1 - n + 1) = n^2$$

$$4n = n^2$$

$$n = 4$$

42. If, on the contrary, $\sqrt{3}$ were rational, then we could write it as a fraction and reduce the fraction to lowest terms. Suppose then that

(*) $$\sqrt{3} = \frac{p}{q} \quad \text{with } \frac{p}{q} \text{ in lowest terms.}$$

Squaring both sides, we have

$$3 = \frac{p^2}{q^2}$$

and therefore

(**) $$3q^2 = p^2.$$

This is an equation between positive integers. Since p^2 is a multiple of 3, p itself must be a multiple of 3 and we can write

$$p = 3n. \quad (\dagger)$$

Substituting 3n for p in (**) we get

$$3q^2 = (3n)^2 = 9n^2,$$

($\dagger$) Integers can take on one of three forms: 3n, 3n+1, 3n+2. If p were of the form 3n+1 or 3n+2, then p^2 would not be a multiple of 3:

$$(3n+1)^2 = 9n^2+6n+1 \quad \text{is not a multiple of 3}$$

and

$$(3n+2)^2 = 9n^2+12n+4 \quad \text{is not a multiple of 3.}$$

and, dividing by 3,

$$q^2 = 3n^2.$$

This last equation tells us that q^2 is a multiple of 3 and therefore that q itself is a multiple of 3. (Same reasoning as before.)

    With p and q both multiples of 3, the fraction p/q can not be in lowest terms. But this is impossible, for by (*) p/q is in lowest terms. The assumption that $\sqrt{3}$ is rational has led to a contradiction. It follows that $\sqrt{3}$ is not rational.

SECTION 2.2

1. $-2, -3$ 2. $2, -3$ 3. $-4, 1$ 4. $\frac{2}{3}$

5. $7, -2$ 6. 3 7. $-\frac{4}{3}, -1$ 8. $\frac{1}{8}, -4$

9. $\frac{1}{4}, \frac{2}{3}$ 10. $\frac{1}{3}, -5$ 11. 9 12. b^2

13. $\frac{1}{16}$ 14. $(\frac{b}{2a})^2 = \frac{b^2}{4a^2}$ 15. $\frac{3}{4}$ 16. $\frac{1}{8}$

17. $5, 7$ 18. $-2 \pm \sqrt{7}$ 19. $-3 \pm \sqrt{3}$ 20. $-\frac{3}{2} \pm \frac{1}{2}\sqrt{3}$

21. $-1 \pm \frac{1}{5}\sqrt{10}$ 22. no real roots

23. $-\frac{1}{2}$ (square already complete)   24. no real roots

25. $-2, \frac{5}{3}$ 26. $-4, \frac{1}{2}$ 27. $-\frac{1}{6} \pm \frac{1}{6}\sqrt{73}$ 28. no real roots

29. $-\frac{5}{32} \pm \frac{1}{32}\sqrt{89}$ 30. $-\frac{1}{3}\sqrt{6}$ (square already complete)

SECTION 2.3

1. $-6 \pm \sqrt{31}$ 2. no real roots   3. $\frac{1}{2}(-11 \pm \sqrt{161})$

4. $-2, -\frac{4}{3}$ 5. $-2, -\frac{3}{2}$ 6. $\frac{1}{2}(1 \pm \sqrt{7})$

7. $\frac{1}{2}(3 \pm \sqrt{15})$ 8. $-4, -\frac{1}{3}$ 9. $-1 \pm \sqrt{11}$

10. no real roots   11. $\frac{1}{2}(5 \pm 5\sqrt{5})$ 12. $\frac{1}{2}(5 \pm \sqrt{105})$

13. $4 \pm 2\sqrt{3}$ 14. $\frac{1}{2}(1 \pm \sqrt{7})$ 15. no real roots

16. no real roots   17. $\frac{1}{3}(-2 \pm \sqrt{19})$ 18. $1 \pm \frac{1}{2}\sqrt{2}$

19. (a) As a quadratic in x, the equation can be written

$$y^2x^2 - 2x + y = 0.$$

The general quadratic formula gives

$$x = \frac{1 \pm \sqrt{1 - y^3}}{y^2}.$$

(b) As a quadratic in y, the equation can be written

$$x^2y^2 + y - 2x = 0.$$

The general qudratic formula gives

$$y = \frac{-1 \pm \sqrt{1 + 8x^3}}{2x^2}.$$

20. If x is one of the numbers, the other must be 21 - x. If the product of the numbers is to be 108, we must have

$$x(21 - x) = 108.$$

This simplifies to

$$x^2 - 21x + 108 = 0.$$

The roots of this equation are 9 and 12.

21. Let x be the length of one of the sides. Then $8 - x$ is the length of an adjacent side. Since the area is to be 11, we must have

$$x(8 - x) = 11.$$

This equation simplifies to

$$x^2 - 8x + 11 = 0$$

and gives $x = 4 \pm \sqrt{5}$. The dimensions of the rectangle are $4 + \sqrt{5}$, $4 - \sqrt{5}$

22. If the length of one leg is x, the length of the other is $8 - x$. By the Pythagorean theorem

$$x^2 + (8 - x)^2 = 36.$$

This simplifies to

$$x^2 - 8x + 14 = 0.$$

The roots are $x = 4 \pm \sqrt{2}$. The legs have lengths $4 + \sqrt{2}$ and $4 - \sqrt{2}$.

23. If one side has length x, the other side has length $15/x$. By the Pythagorean theorem

$$x^2 + \left(\frac{15}{x}\right)^2 = 34,$$

which simplifies to

$$x^4 - 34x^2 + 225 = 0.$$

This is a quadratic in x^2 that we can solve for x^2 by applying the general quadratic formula. Doing this, we find that

$$x^2 = 25 \quad \text{or} \quad x^2 = 9.$$

Thus $x = 5$ or $x = 3$. The dimensions are 5 and 3.

24. Let x be the length of one of the sides. The length of an adjacent side is then $\frac{1}{2}P - x$. Since the area is A, we must have

$$x(\tfrac{1}{2}P - x) = A.$$

This equation can be written

$$x^2 - \tfrac{1}{2}Px + A = 0.$$

The general quadratic formula gives, after simplification,

$$x = \frac{P \pm \sqrt{P^2 - 16A}}{4}.$$

The lengths of the sides are

$$\frac{P + \sqrt{P^2 - 16A}}{4} \quad \text{and} \quad \frac{P - \sqrt{P^2 - 16A}}{4}.$$

25. Let x be the length of one of the legs. Then $P - c - x$ is the length of the other. By the Pythagorean theorem

$$x^2 + (P - c - x)^2 = c^2.$$

The equation can be written

$$2x^2 - 2(P - c)x + (P - c)^2 - c^2 = 0.$$

By the general quadratic formula

$$x = \frac{2(P - c) \pm \sqrt{4(P - c)^2 - 8[(P - c)^2 - c^2]}}{4}.$$

This simplifies to

$$x = \frac{P - c \pm \sqrt{2c^2 - (P - c)^2}}{2}.$$

The lengths of the legs are

$$\frac{P - c + \sqrt{2c^2 - (P - c)^2}}{2} \quad \text{and} \quad \frac{P - c - \sqrt{2c^2 - (P - c)^2}}{2}.$$

26. If one side has length x, the other side has length A/x.
     By the Pythagorean theorem

$$x^2 + \left(\frac{A}{x}\right)^2 = d^2,$$

which simplifies to

$$x^4 - d^2x^2 + A^2 = 0.$$

This is a quadratic in x^2 that we can solve for x^2 by the
general quadratic formula. Doing this, we find that

$$x^2 = \frac{d^2 \pm \sqrt{d^4 - 4A^2}}{2}.$$

The lengths of the sides of the rectangle are

$$\sqrt{\frac{d^2 + \sqrt{d^4 - 4A^2}}{2}} \quad \text{and} \quad \sqrt{\frac{d^2 - \sqrt{d^4 - 4A^2}}{2}}.$$

SECTION 2.4

1. 0, 0.333, $\frac{1}{3}$, 0.334, $\frac{1}{\sqrt{3}}$, 1, 1.142, 1.41, $\sqrt{2}$

2. $\dfrac{1}{1 - \sqrt{2}}$, $\dfrac{1}{1 - \sqrt{3}}$, $1 - \sqrt{3}$, $-\dfrac{1}{\sqrt{2}}$, $-\dfrac{1}{\sqrt{3}}$, $1 - \sqrt{2}$, $\sqrt{2}$, $\sqrt{3}$

3. $2a < 2b$ 　　　　4. $2b < 3b$ 　　　　5. $-2a > -2b$

6. $-b > -2b$ 　　　　7. $-2a > -3b$ 　　　　8. $ab > a^2$

9. $-2a^2 > -2b^2$ 　　　10. $-2a^2 > -3b^2$ 　　　11. $1 - ab < 1 - a^2$

12. $2a < 2b$ 　　　　13. $2b > 3b$ 　　　　14. $-2a > 3b$

15. $-2a > -2b$ 16. $a^2 > b^2$ 17. $ab > b^2$

18. To get from

$$\frac{a}{b} < \frac{c}{d} \quad \text{to} \quad ad < bc,$$

multiply the inequality on the left by bd. To go the other way, multiply the inequality on the right by 1/bd.

19. $\dfrac{1}{\sqrt{a}} > \dfrac{1}{\sqrt{b}}$ 20. $\dfrac{a}{\sqrt{b}} < \dfrac{b}{\sqrt{a}}$ 21. $\dfrac{b}{\sqrt{a}+b} > \dfrac{a}{\sqrt{b}+a}$

22. $\sqrt{\dfrac{x}{x+1}} < \sqrt{\dfrac{x+1}{x+2}}$

23. series connection: $\dfrac{1}{\dfrac{1}{R_1} + \dfrac{1}{R_2}} < \dfrac{1}{\dfrac{1}{R_1}} = R_1 < R_1 + R_2$

24. decreased: $\dfrac{1}{\dfrac{1}{R_1} + \cdots + \dfrac{1}{R_n} + \dfrac{1}{R_{n+1}}} < \dfrac{1}{\dfrac{1}{R_1} + \cdots + \dfrac{1}{R_n}}$

as you can verify by cross multiplication (2.4.7).

25. $\dfrac{1}{\dfrac{1}{R_1} + \dfrac{1}{R_2} + \cdots + \dfrac{1}{R_n}} < \dfrac{1}{\dfrac{1}{R_1}} = R_1$; similarly for R_2, R_3,etc.

26. (a) $\dfrac{1}{x}$, $\dfrac{1}{\sqrt{x}}$, 1, $\sqrt{x}$, x   (b) x, $\sqrt{x}$, 1, $\dfrac{1}{\sqrt{x}}$, $\dfrac{1}{x}$

27. true:

$$a < b \;\rightarrow\; a - a < b - a \;\rightarrow\; 0 < b - a \;\rightarrow\; b - a > 0$$

|____ by (2.4.4)

$$b - a > 0 \;\rightarrow\; (b - a) + a > 0 + a \;\rightarrow\; b > a \;\rightarrow\; a < b$$

|____ by (2.4.3)

28. false: $-2 < 0$ but $(-2)^2 \not< 0^2$

29. true:

$$\frac{a}{b} > 0 \;\rightarrow\; \frac{a}{b} > 0 \text{ and } b^2 > 0 \;\rightarrow\; \frac{a}{b}(b^2) > 0(b^2) \;\rightarrow\; ab > 0$$

by (2.4.5)____|

$$ab > 0 \;\rightarrow\; ab > 0 \text{ and } \frac{1}{b^2} > 0 \;\rightarrow\; ab\!\left(\frac{1}{b^2}\right) > 0\!\left(\frac{1}{b^2}\right) \;\rightarrow\; \frac{a}{b} > 0$$

by (2.4.5)____|

30. false: $2(0) \geq 0$ but $\dfrac{2}{0}$ is undefined

31. If $a = 0$ or $a = b$, the result is obvious. If $0 < a < b$, the result follows by cross multiplication (2.4.7).

32. $$\frac{a}{1 + a} \leq \frac{b + c}{1 + b + c} = \frac{b}{1 + b + c} + \frac{c}{1 + b + c} \leq \frac{b}{1 + b} + \frac{c}{1 + c}$$

|____ by Exercise 31

SECTION 2.5

1. {-1,0,1,2}   2. {0}   3. {-1,0,1,2,3,4}

4. {1}   5. {0,2,4,6,8,···}   6. {2,4}

7. Φ   8. {±2,±4,±6,±8,···} 9. Φ

10. A   11. C   12. set of all real
                                         numbers

13. {x: 3 < x ≤ 4}   14. {x: 3 < x ≤ 4}   15. A

16. (a) B   (b) A

17. (a) B ⊆ A   (b) A ⊆ B   (c) A = B

18. (a) 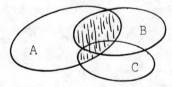   (b)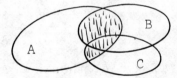

(c) 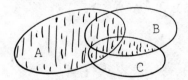   (d)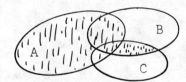

$A \cap (B \cup C) = (A \cap B) \cup (A \cap C),$

$A \cup (B \cap C) = (A \cup B) \cap (A \cup C)$

19. (a) First we show that A ∩ (B ∪ C) ⊆ (A ∩ B) ∪ (A ∩ C):

$$x \in A \cap (B \cup C) \to x \in A \text{ and } x \in B \cup C$$

$$\to x \in A \text{ and } x \in B \text{ or } x \in A \text{ and } x \in C$$

$$\to x \in A \cap B \text{ or } x \in A \cap C$$

$$\to x \in (A \cap B) \cup (A \cap C).$$

Now we show that (A ∩ B) ∪ (A ∩ C) ⊆ A ∩ (B ∪ C):

$$x \in (A \cap B) \cup (A \cap C) \to x \in A \cap B \text{ or } x \in A \cap C$$

$$\to x \in A \text{ and } x \in B \text{ or } x \in A \text{ and } x \in C$$

$$\to x \in A \text{ and } x \in B \text{ or } x \in C$$

$$\to x \in A \cap (B \cup C).$$

(b) First we show that A ∪ (B ∩ C) ⊆ (A ∪ B) ∩ (A ∪ C):

$$x \in A \cup (B \cap C) \to x \in A \text{ or } x \in B \cap C$$

$$\to x \in A \text{ or } x \in B \text{ and } x \in C.$$

If x ∈ A, then x ∈ A ∪ B, x ∈ A ∪ C and

$$x \in (A \cup B) \cap (A \cup C).$$

If x ∈ B and x ∈ C, then x ∈ A ∪ B, x ∈ A ∪ C and

$$x \in (A \cup B) \cap (A \cup C).$$

In either case

$$x \in (A \cup B) \cap (A \cup C).$$

Now we show that (A ∪ B) ∩ (A ∪ C) ⊆ A ∪ (B ∩ C):

$$x \in (A \cup B) \cap (A \cup C) \to x \in A \cup B \text{ and } x \in A \cup C$$

$$\to x \in A \text{ or } x \in B \text{ and } x \in A \text{ or } x \in C.$$

If $x \notin A$, then $x \in B$ and $x \in C$, and therefore

$$x \in A \cup (B \cap C).$$

If $x \in A$, then $x \in A \cup (B \cap C)$. In either case

$$x \in A \cup (B \cap C).$$

20. 2^n *Justification.* Each element gives two possibilities: either we put it in the subset or we don't. There are n elements, thus 2^n possibilities in all.

21. $k(k - 1)(k - 2)\cdots(2)(1)$ *Justification.* There are k possibilities for the first position, $k - 1$ possibilities for the second position, etc.

22. $n(n - 1)(n - 2)\cdots(n - k + 1)$

23. Let N_k be the number of subsets of k elements that can be made from a set with n elements, and let n_k be the number of arrangements of length k that can be made from that same set of n elements.

   Since every set of k elements yields k! arrangements of length k (Exercise 21),

$$n_k = N_k \cdot k!$$

By Exercise 22

$$n_k = n(n - 1)\cdots(n - k + 1).$$

Thus

$$n(n - 1)\cdots(n - k + 1) = N_k \cdot k!$$

and

$$N_k = \frac{n(n - 1)\cdots(n - k + 1)}{k!}.$$

24. (a) $2^6 = 64$ (b) $6! = 720$ (c) $6 \cdot 5 \cdot 4 \cdot 3 = 360$ (d) 15

SECTION 2.6

1. $(0,2)$ 2. $(\frac{1}{2},1)$ 3. Φ 4. $(0,1]$

5. $[0,2]$ 6. $(\frac{1}{2},1]$ 7. $[0,1]$ 8. $[0,2]$

9. $(-3,\infty)$ 10. $[-2,0)$ 11. $[-2,3)$ 12. $(-\infty,\infty)$

13. $[0,1]$ 14. $\{0\}$ 15. $[\frac{3}{2},2]$ 16. $[0,\infty)$

17. $[-1,1]$ 18. $[-\frac{1}{4},\frac{1}{4}]$ 19. $(-\infty,0) \cup (0,\infty)$

20. $(-\infty,0) \cup (0,1) \cup (1,\infty)$ 21. $(0,1) \cup (1,2) \cup (2,\infty)$

22. $(-\infty,-3) \cup (-3,0) \cup (0,3) \cup (3,\infty)$

23. $a + \frac{1}{4}(b - a)$, $a + \frac{2}{4}(b - a)$, $a + \frac{3}{4}(b - a)$

24. $a + \frac{1}{5}(b - a)$, $a + \frac{2}{5}(b - a)$, $a + \frac{3}{5}(b - a)$, $a + \frac{4}{5}(b - a)$

25. (a) $n - 1$ (b) $a + \frac{1}{n}(b - a)$, $a + \frac{2}{n}(b - a), \cdots, a + \frac{n-1}{n}(b-a)$

26. (a) $\frac{7}{2}$ (b) $3, 4$ (c) $\frac{11}{4}, \frac{14}{4}, \frac{17}{4}$ (d) $\frac{17}{7}, \frac{20}{7}, \frac{23}{7}, \frac{26}{7}, \frac{29}{7}, \frac{32}{7}$

27. (a) $\frac{3}{2}$ (b) $\frac{1}{3}, \frac{8}{3}$ (c) $-\frac{1}{4}, \frac{6}{4}, \frac{13}{4}$ (d) $-1, 0, 1, 2, 3, 4$

28. (a) If $x \in [a,b]$, then x can be written in the form

$$a + t(b - a) \quad \text{with} \quad t \in [0,1]$$

by setting

$$t = \frac{x - a}{b - a}.$$

If $t \in [0,1]$, then $a + t(b - a) \in [a,b]$ as can be seen by noting that

$$a = a + 0(b - a) \le a + t(b - a) \le a + 1(b - a) = b.$$

(b) $a + t(b - a)$ with (i) $t \in (0,1)$ (ii) $t \in [0,\infty)$

(iii) $t \in (0,\infty)$ (iv) $t \in (-\infty,0]$ (v) $t \in (-\infty,0)$

SECTION 2.7

1. $(-\infty,1)$ 2. $[2,\infty)$ 3. $(-\infty,-3]$

4. $(-\frac{7}{2},\infty)$ 5. $[-1,\infty)$ 6. $(-\infty,\frac{9}{2})$

7. $(-2,\infty)$ 8. $[-1,2]$ 9. $(-1,1)$

10. $(-2,2)$ 11. $(-\infty,-1) \cup (1,\infty)$ 12. $(-\infty,-2) \cup (2,\infty)$

13. $[-4,4]$ 14. $(-\infty,-4] \cup [4,\infty)$ 15. $(1,4)$

16. $[-2,1]$ 17. $(-\infty,1) \cup (2,\infty)$ 18. $(-5,-4)$

19. $(-\infty,\infty)$ 20. $\{2\}$ 21. $(-\infty,-\frac{1}{5})$

22. $(\frac{5}{24},\infty)$ 23. $(-3,3)$ 24. $\{a\}$

25. $(-\infty,a) \cup (a+1,\infty)$ 26. $[2-\sqrt{6},2+\sqrt{6}]$ 27. $(-5-2\sqrt{6},-5+2\sqrt{6})$

28. $(-\infty,-2-\sqrt{2}] \cup [-2+\sqrt{2},\infty)$ 29. $(-\infty,0) \cup (0,\infty)$

30. $[-6,0]$ 31. $(-\infty,0)$ 32. $(-1,1)$

33. $(-\infty,0) \cup (0,1)$ 34. $(-\infty,0) \cup (0,\frac{3}{2})$ 35. $(0,1)$

36. $(0,10)$ 37. $(0,1) \cup (2,\infty)$ 38. $(-\infty,0) \cup (1,2)$

39. $(-\infty,1) \cup (2,3)$ 40. $(-\infty,0] \cup [\frac{1}{2},\frac{5}{3}]$

SECTION 2.8

1. $(-\infty, 2)$ 2. $(-2, \infty)$ 3. $(0, 1)$

4. $(2, 5)$ 5. $(5, \infty)$ 6. $(4, 5)$

7. $(-\infty, -\frac{5}{3}) \cup (5, \infty)$ 8. $(-\infty, -2) \cup (1, 2)$ 9. $(1, \infty)$

10. $(-\infty, \frac{5}{3}) \cup (\frac{11}{6}, \infty)$ 11. $(\frac{3}{2}, \frac{7}{4})$ 12. $(-\infty, \frac{1}{2}) \cup (\frac{2}{3}, \infty)$

13. $(1, 2)$ 14. $(-\infty, 2)$

15. $(-1-\sqrt{2}, 0) \cup (\sqrt{2}-1, \infty)$ 16. $(0, \frac{5}{3}) \cup (\frac{5}{2}, \infty)$

17. $(-1, 0) \cup (1, \infty)$ 18. $(-\frac{5}{3}, -1) \cup (\frac{5}{2}, \infty)$

19. $(-\infty, -n-1) \cup (-1, 0)$ 20. $(-n-1, -1) \cup (-1, -\frac{n+1}{2n+1})$

SECTION 2.9

1. 4 2. $\frac{3}{2}$ 3. $3, 5$ 4. $1, 2$

5. $-3, -\frac{1}{3}$ 6. $\frac{1}{3}, 3$ 7. ϕ 8. $-3, \frac{17}{5}$

9. ± 1 10. $0, 1, 2$ 11. $(3, 5)$ 12. $(1, 2)$

13. $[1, 5]$ 14. $(-\infty, 1) \cup (5, \infty)$ 15. ϕ

16. set of all real numbers   17. $(-\frac{3}{2}, \frac{5}{2})$

18. $(-\infty, -\frac{3}{2}) \cup (\frac{5}{2}, \infty)$ 19. $(-\infty, -\frac{1}{4}] \cup [\frac{7}{4}, \infty)$

20. $(-\frac{1}{4}, \frac{7}{4})$ 21. $[-\frac{7}{2}, \frac{5}{2}]$ 22. $(-\infty, 1] \cup [5, \infty)$

23. $(\frac{7}{10}, \frac{9}{10})$ 24. $(-\infty, -\frac{11}{8}] \cup [-\frac{9}{8}, \infty)$ 25. ϕ

26. $[0, \infty)$ 27. $(-\infty, \infty)$ 28. $(-\infty, 0)$ 29. $(-\infty, \frac{3}{2})$

30. $(-\infty, -1]$ 31. $(\frac{3}{2}, \infty)$ 32. $(-\infty, \frac{5}{2})$

33. $(-\sqrt{5}, -\sqrt{3}) \cup (\sqrt{3}, \sqrt{5})$ 34. $(-\infty, -\sqrt{5}] \cup [-\sqrt{3}, \sqrt{3}] \cup [\sqrt{5}, \infty)$

35. $(-\infty, -\sqrt{3}) \cup (\sqrt{3}, \infty)$ 36. $[-\sqrt{3}, \sqrt{3}]$

37. for x > 0   for x < 0

$$\frac{x}{|x|} = \frac{x}{x} = 1; \qquad\qquad \frac{x}{|x|} = \frac{x}{-x} = -1.$$

38. for x > 0   for x < 0

$$\frac{x^2 - x|x|}{|x|} = \frac{x^2 - x^2}{x} = 0; \qquad \frac{x^2 - x|x|}{|x|} = \frac{x^2 - x(-x)}{-x} = \frac{2x^2}{-x}$$

$$= -2x.$$

39. if a and b have the same sign, or if a or b is 0

40. $\left| \,|a| - |b| \,\right|^2 = (|a| - |b|)^2$

$$= |a|^2 - 2|a||b| + |b|^2$$

$$= a^2 - 2|ab| + b^2$$

$$\leq a^2 - 2ab + b^2 = (a - b)^2 = |a - b|^2.$$

The desired result follows by taking square roots.

41. $\frac{1}{3}\varepsilon$ 42. $\frac{1}{2}\varepsilon$ 43. $\frac{1}{5}\varepsilon$ 44. 2ε

SECTION 2.10

1. $\dfrac{1}{3 - 2\sqrt{5}} = \dfrac{1}{3 - 2\sqrt{5}} \cdot \dfrac{3 + 2\sqrt{5}}{3 + 2\sqrt{5}} = \dfrac{3 + 2\sqrt{5}}{-11} = -\dfrac{1}{11}(3 + 2\sqrt{5})$

2. $\dfrac{1}{2\sqrt{2} + \sqrt{5}} = \dfrac{1}{2\sqrt{2} + \sqrt{5}} \cdot \dfrac{2\sqrt{2} - \sqrt{5}}{2\sqrt{2} - \sqrt{5}} = \dfrac{2\sqrt{2} - \sqrt{5}}{3} = \dfrac{1}{3}(2\sqrt{2} - \sqrt{5})$

3. $\dfrac{2}{1 + \sqrt{3}} = \dfrac{2}{1 + \sqrt{3}} \cdot \dfrac{1 - \sqrt{3}}{1 - \sqrt{3}} = \dfrac{2(1 - \sqrt{3})}{-2} = \sqrt{3} - 1$

4. $\dfrac{\sqrt{2}}{1 - \sqrt{2}} = \dfrac{\sqrt{2}}{1 - \sqrt{2}} \cdot \dfrac{1 + \sqrt{2}}{1 + \sqrt{2}} = \dfrac{\sqrt{2} + 2}{-1} = -\sqrt{2} - 2$

5. $\dfrac{1}{(1 + \sqrt{2})(1 - \sqrt{5})} = \dfrac{1}{(1 + \sqrt{2})(1 - \sqrt{5})} \cdot \dfrac{(1 - \sqrt{2})(1 + \sqrt{5})}{(1 - \sqrt{2})(1 + \sqrt{5})}$

$= \dfrac{(1 - \sqrt{2})(1 + \sqrt{5})}{(-1)(-4)} = \dfrac{1}{4}(1 - \sqrt{2})(1 + \sqrt{5})$

6. $\dfrac{8}{(1 - \sqrt{2})(1 + \sqrt{5})} = \dfrac{8}{(1 - \sqrt{2})(1 + \sqrt{5})} \cdot \dfrac{(1 + \sqrt{2})(1 - \sqrt{5})}{(1 + \sqrt{2})(1 - \sqrt{5})}$

$= \dfrac{8(1 + \sqrt{2})(1 - \sqrt{5})}{(-1)(-4)} = 2(1 + \sqrt{2})(1 - \sqrt{5})$

7. $\sqrt{\dfrac{3}{5}} - \sqrt{\dfrac{5}{3}} = \dfrac{1}{5}\sqrt{15} - \dfrac{1}{3}\sqrt{15} = -\dfrac{2}{15}\sqrt{15}$

8. $\sqrt{\dfrac{9}{5}} + \sqrt{\dfrac{5}{4}} = \dfrac{3}{5}\sqrt{5} + \dfrac{1}{2}\sqrt{5} = \dfrac{11}{10}\sqrt{5}$

9. $\dfrac{1}{4}, \ \dfrac{4}{3}$

10. $-\sqrt{5}$

11. $-8 \pm \sqrt{67}$

12. no real roots

13. $-\dfrac{3}{4}$

14. $-\dfrac{3}{2}, \ 2$

15. no real roots

16. $-\dfrac{1}{2}\sqrt{5}, \ \sqrt{2}$

17. $(-\infty, 5)$

18. $(-\infty, -9]$

19. $[-\dfrac{4}{9}, \infty)$

20. $(-\infty, -\dfrac{2}{3}]$

21. $(-\infty, -4] \cup [5, \infty)$

22. $(-4, 5)$

23. $[-\dfrac{3}{2}, \dfrac{3}{2}]$

24. ϕ

25. $(-\infty,-4) \cup (\frac{5}{2},\infty)$ 26. $(2 - 2\sqrt{2}, 2 + 2\sqrt{2})$ 27. $(\frac{2}{5},\frac{6}{5})$

28. $(-\infty,-2] \cup [-\frac{1}{2},\infty)$ 29. $(-\infty,-1) \cup (3,\infty)$ 30. $(-3,-2)$

31. (a) the swing time is shortened

    (b) the swing time is lengthened

32. (a) lengthen the arm by 21%: $(1.1)^2 = 1.21$

    (b) lengthen the arm by 44%: $(1.2)^2 = 1.44$

33. (a) shorten the arm by 19%: $(0.9)^2 = 0.81$

    (b) shorten the arm by 36%: $(0.8)^2 = 0.64$

34. $\ell = \dfrac{gT^2}{\pi^2}$ 35. (a) $\ell = \dfrac{g}{\pi^2}$ (b) $\ell \cong \dfrac{32}{(3.14)^2} \cong 3.25 \text{ ft}$

    $= 3 \text{ ft } 3 \text{ in}$

36. $(-\sqrt{5},-\sqrt{3}) \cup (\sqrt{3},\sqrt{5})$ 37. $(-\infty,-4) \cup (-2,2) \cup (4,\infty)$

38. $(-2,-1) \cup (1,\infty)$ 39. $(-\infty,-\frac{1}{2}) \cup (1,3)$ 40. $(-\frac{1}{3},0)$

41. $(-\frac{1}{2},-\frac{1}{3})$ 42. $(-\infty, \dfrac{3-\sqrt{5}}{2}) \cup (1,2) \cup (\dfrac{3+\sqrt{5}}{2}, \infty)$

43. $(1,2)$ 44. $-2, -1, 1, 2$

45. $(-2,-1) \cup (1,2)$ 46. $(\frac{1}{3},1)$ 47. $(-\infty,\frac{1}{2})$

48. With $a < 0 < b$,

$a^2|b^2| - 2ab|ab| = a^2b^2 - 2ab|a||b|$

$= a^2b^2 - 2ab(-a)(b) = a^2b^2 + 2a^2b^2 = 3a^2b^2.$

49. For all real numbers a and b,

$$0 \le (a - b)^2 = a^2 - 2ab + b^2$$

so that

$$2ab \le a^2 + b^2$$

and consequently

$$ab \le \frac{1}{2}(a^2 + b^2).$$

50. With $r < 0$ and $a < b$,

$$a = \frac{a + ra}{1 + r} < \frac{a + rb}{1 + r} < \frac{b + rb}{1 + r} = b.$$

51. $x = 0$: For $x \ge 0$,

$$(\sqrt{x^2} + 1)(x - 1) = (x + 1)(x - 1) = x^2 - 1$$

and the equation reads

$$x^2 - 1 = -1.$$

This simplifies to $x^2 = 0$ and gives $x = 0$.
    For $x < 0$,

$$(\sqrt{x^2} + 1)(x - 1) = (-x + 1)(x - 1) = -(x - 1)^2$$

and the equation reads

$$-(x - 1)^2 = -1.$$

This simplifies to $(x - 1)^2 = 1$. This equation has no negative roots. Its only roots are 0 and 2.

52. On the one hand the area of the total square is

$$(a + b)^2 = a^2 + 2ab + b^2;$$

on the other hand the area of the total square is

$$c^2 + 4(\tfrac{1}{2}ab) = c^2 + 2ab.$$

Obviously then

$$a^2 + 2ab + b^2 = c^2 + 2ab$$

and thus

$$a^2 + b^2 = c^2.$$

53. (a) $w\sqrt{h^2 + \ell^2}$, $h\sqrt{w^2 + \ell^2}$, $\ell\sqrt{w^2 + h^2}$

(b) $w\sqrt{h^2 + \ell^2} < h\sqrt{w^2 + \ell^2} < \ell\sqrt{w^2 + h^2}$:

PROOF. Since $w < h < \ell$ and these numbers are all positive,

$$w^2 < h^2 < \ell^2.$$

It follows that

$$w^2h^2 + w^2\ell^2 < w^2h^2 + h^2\ell^2 < w^2\ell^2 + h^2\ell^2,$$

$$w^2(h^2 + \ell^2) < h^2(w^2 + \ell^2) < \ell^2(w^2 + h^2),$$

$$w\sqrt{h^2 + \ell^2} < h\sqrt{w^2 + \ell^2} < \ell\sqrt{w^2 + h^2}.$$

54. (a) PROOF. Suppose that x_0 is a root of the quadratic equation. Then

$$ax^2 + bx + c = (ax^2 + bx + c) - (ax_0^2 + bx_0 + c)$$

$$= a(x^2 - x_0^2) + b(x - x_0)$$

$$= [a(x + x_0) + b](x - x_0).$$

(b) By part (a), the other root is a root of the equation

$$a(x + x_0) + b = 0.$$

Dividing by a we have

$$x + x_0 + \frac{b}{a} = 0$$

so that

$$x = -x_0 - \frac{b}{a}.$$

If x_0 is one root, the other root is $-x_0 - \dfrac{b}{a}$.

(c) From the proof of part (a)

$$ax^2 + bx + c = [ax + (ax_0 + b)](x - x_0).$$

(d) By part (b)

$$x_0 + x_1 = x_0 + (-x_0 - \frac{b}{a}) = -\frac{b}{a}$$

$$x_0 x_1 = x_0(-x_0 - \frac{b}{a}) = \frac{x_0(-ax_0 - b)}{a}$$

$$= \frac{-ax_0^2 - bx_0}{a}$$

$$ax_0^2 + bx_0 + c = 0 \qquad \qquad \Bigg| \quad = \frac{c}{a} \quad .$$

Another method:

$$\frac{-b + \sqrt{b^2 - 4ac}}{2a} + \frac{-b - \sqrt{b^2 - 4ac}}{2a} = -\frac{2b}{2a} = -\frac{b}{a}$$

$$(\frac{-b + \sqrt{b^2 - 4ac}}{2a})(\frac{-b - \sqrt{b^2 - 4ac}}{2a}) = \frac{b^2 - b^2 + 4ac}{4a^2} = \frac{c}{a}$$

55. From the figure

$$a^2 - (b - x)^2 = h^2 \qquad \text{and} \qquad c^2 - x^2 = h^2.$$

Set

$$a^2 - (b - x)^2 = c^2 - x^2$$

and you'll find that

$$x = \frac{c^2 + b^2 - a^2}{2b}.$$

Thus

$$h = \sqrt{c^2 - x^2} = \sqrt{c^2 - \frac{(c^2 + b^2 - a^2)^2}{4b^2}} = \frac{1}{2b}\sqrt{4b^2 c^2 - (c^2 + b^2 - a^2)^2}$$

and

$$A = \frac{1}{2}bh = \frac{1}{4}\sqrt{4b^2c^2 - (c^2+b^2-a^2)^2}$$

$$= \frac{1}{4}\sqrt{(2bc+c^2+b^2-a^2)(2bc-c^2-b^2+a^2)}$$

$$= \frac{1}{4}\sqrt{[(b+c)^2 - a^2][a^2 - (b-c)^2]}$$

$$= \frac{1}{4}\sqrt{(b+c+a)(b+c-a)(a+b-c)(a-b+c)}$$

$$= \frac{1}{4}\sqrt{(a+b+c)(a+b+c-2a)(a+b+c-2b)(a+b+c-2c)}$$

$$= \frac{1}{4}\sqrt{p(p-2a)(p-2b)(p-2c)}$$

$$= \sqrt{\frac{p(p-2a)(p-2b)(p-2c)}{16}}$$

$$= \sqrt{\frac{p}{2}(\frac{p}{2} - a)(\frac{p}{2} - b)(\frac{p}{2} - c)} = \sqrt{s(s-a)(s-b)(s-c)}.$$

56. The following statements are equivalent:

$$a\sqrt{1 - \left(\frac{a^2+c^2-b^2}{2ac}\right)^2} = b\sqrt{1 - \left(\frac{b^2+c^2-a^2}{2bc}\right)^2}$$

$$\frac{a\sqrt{4a^2c^2 - (a^2+c^2-b^2)^2}}{2ac} = \frac{b\sqrt{4b^2c^2 - (b^2+c^2-a^2)^2}}{2bc}$$

$$\sqrt{4a^2c^2 - (a^2+c^2-b^2)^2} = \sqrt{4b^2c^2 - (b^2+c^2-a^2)^2}.$$

Observe that

$$4a^2c^2 - (a^2+c^2-b^2)^2 = (2ac+a^2+c^2-b^2)(2ac-a^2-c^2+b^2)$$

$$= [(a+c)^2 - b^2][b^2 - (a-c)^2]$$

$$= (a+c+b)(a+c-b)(b+a-c)(b-a+c).$$

As you can check, $4b^2c^2 - (b^2+c^2-a^2)^2$ is the product of the same four factors.

SECTION 3.1

1. (a) II   (b) I   (c) IV   (d) III

2. (a) $(2,3)$ (b) $(-2,-3)$ (c) $(-2,3)$

3. (a) $(-\frac{1}{2},-\frac{1}{3})$ (b) $(\frac{1}{2},\frac{1}{3})$ (c) $(\frac{1}{2},-\frac{1}{3})$ 4. $(\frac{3}{2},-4)$

5. (a) $(2,1)$ (b) $(2,-2)$ (c) $(\frac{1+\sqrt{2}}{2}, -\frac{1+\sqrt{2}}{2})$

6. $(-1,6)$; $(2,2)$ 7. $(-2,-18)$

8. $(\frac{1}{2}\sqrt{3}b,\frac{1}{2}b)$ or $(-\frac{1}{2}\sqrt{3}b,\frac{1}{2}b)$:

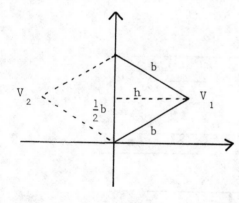

possible vertices V_1, V_2

The coordinates Of V_1 are $(h,\frac{1}{2}b)$. To find h we use the Pythagorean theorem

$$h = \sqrt{b^2-(\tfrac{1}{2}b)^2} = \sqrt{\tfrac{3}{4}b^2} = \tfrac{1}{2}\sqrt{3}b.$$

The coordinates of V_1 are thus $(\frac{1}{2}\sqrt{3}b,\frac{1}{2}b)$. The coordinates of V_2 can be obtained by symmetry.

9. (a) $r = -1$, $s = \frac{1}{3}$ (b) $r = -\frac{1}{3}$, $s = 1$ (c) $r = -\frac{1}{3}$, $s = \frac{1}{3}$

10. (a) midpt of $\overline{PQ} = (-\frac{1}{2},1)$ (b) midpt of median to $\overline{PQ} = (\frac{5}{4},\frac{1}{2})$

       midpt of $\overline{QR} = (\frac{3}{2},1)$ midpt of median to $\overline{QR} = (\frac{1}{4},\frac{1}{2})$

       midpt of $\overline{PR} = (1,0)$ midpt of median to $\overline{PR} = (\frac{1}{2},1)$

11. $(x_1 + \frac{1}{3}(x_2 - x_1), y_1 + \frac{1}{3}(y_2 - y_1))$, $(x_1 + \frac{2}{3}(x_2 - x_1), y_1 + \frac{2}{3}(y_2 - y_1))$

To show this, we refer to the figure below.   The points of trisection are marked T_1 and T_2.

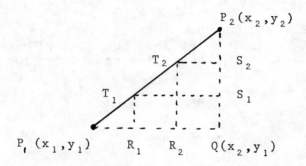

$\Delta P_1 Q P_2$ is similar to $\Delta P_1 R_1 T_1$ and to $\Delta P_1 R_2 T_2$.   Since T_1 and T_2 trisect $\overline{P_1 P_2}$, the points R_1 and R_2 trisect $\overline{P_1 Q}$, and the points S_1 and S_2 trisect $\overline{Q P_2}$.   Obviously then

the x-coordinate of T_1 = the x-coordinate of R_1 = $x_1 + \frac{1}{3}(x_2 - x_1)$

the y-coordinate of T_1 = the y-coordinate of S_1 = $y_1 + \frac{1}{3}(y_2 - y_1)$

and

the x-coordinate of T_2 = the x-coordinate of R_2 = $x_1 + \frac{2}{3}(x_2 - x_1)$

the y-coordinate of T_2 = the y-coordinate of S_2 = $y_1 + \frac{2}{3}(y_2 - y_1)$

12. $T_1(1,4)$, $T_2(5,2)$ (by similar triangles)

13.   Let the vertices of the triangle be $P_1(x_1,y_1)$, $P_2(x_2,y_2)$, $P_3(x_3,y_3)$.   The midpts of the opposite sides are respectively

$M_1(\frac{1}{2}(x_2 + x_3), \frac{1}{2}(y_2 + y_3))$, $M_2(\frac{1}{2}(x_1 + x_3), \frac{1}{2}(y_1 + y_3))$,

$M_3(\frac{1}{2}(x_1 + x_2), \frac{1}{2}(y_1 + y_2))$.

The point of trisection of $\overline{P_1 M_1}$ that is closer to M_1 has x-coordinate

$$x_1 + \frac{2}{3}(\frac{1}{2}(x_2 + x_3) - x_1) = \frac{1}{3}(3x_1 + x_2 + x_3 - 2x_1) = \frac{1}{3}(x_1 + x_2 + x_3)$$

and y-coordinate

$$y_1 + \frac{2}{3}(\frac{1}{2}(y_2 + y_3) - y_1) = \frac{1}{3}(3y_1 + y_2 + y_3 - 2y_1) = \frac{1}{3}(y_1 + y_2 + y_3).$$

Similar calculations show that the point of trisection of $\overline{P_2M_2}$ that is closer to M_2 and the point of trisection of $\overline{P_3M_3}$ that is closer to M_3 have these same coordinates.

SECTION 3.2

1. (a) $\sqrt{26}$ (b) 3   (c) $\sqrt{x_0^2 + y_0^2}$ (d) $\sqrt{x_0^2 + y_0^2}$

2. (a) $d(P,Q) = \sqrt{(a+2)^2 + (0+4)^2} = \sqrt{a^2 + 4a + 20}$,

$$d(P,R) = \sqrt{(a-4)^2 + (0-3)^2} = \sqrt{a^2 - 8a + 25}$$

$$\sqrt{a^2 + 4a + 20} = \sqrt{a^2 - 8a + 25}$$

$$a^2 + 4a + 20 = a^2 - 8a + 25$$

$$12a = 5$$

$$a = \frac{5}{12}$$

(b) $d(P,Q) = \sqrt{(-2-0)^2 + (-4-b)^2} = \sqrt{20 + 8b + b^2}$,

$$d(P,R) = \sqrt{(4-0)^2 + (3-b)^2} = \sqrt{25 - 6b + b^2}$$

$$\sqrt{20 + 8b + b^2} = \sqrt{25 - 6b + b^2}$$

$$20 + 8b + b^2 = 25 - 6b + b^2$$

$$14b = 5$$

$$b = \frac{5}{14}$$

3. (a) yes   (b) yes   (c) no

4. (a) $(x-1)^2 + (y-2)^2 = 4$ (b) $(x+1)^2 + (y+2)^2 = 4$

    (c) $x^2 + y^2 = 49$ (d) $(x+4)^2 + (y-5)^2 = 49$

5. P_1, P_2, P_3

6. (a) $(x-2)^2 + (y+1)^2 = 2$ (b) $(x-1)^2 + (y+2)^2 = 2$

7. (a) $x^2 + y^2 - 8x - 2y + 13 = 0$

     $(x^2-8x+\quad) + (y^2-2y+\quad) = -13$

     $(x^2-8x+16) + (y^2-2y+1) = 4$ (b) radius 1; center $(-3,-2)$

               $(x-4)^2 + (y-1)^2 = 2^2$ (c) radius 10; center $(-\sqrt{2},-\sqrt{3})$

     radius 2; center $(4,1)$ (d) radius 2; center $(\frac{1}{2},-\frac{1}{2})$

8. There are two possibilities for R:

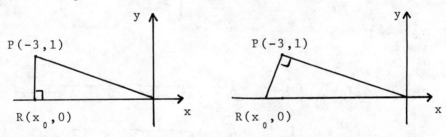

The first case gives $x_0 = -3$. In the second case,

$$[(x_0+3)^2 + (0-1)^2] + [(0+3)^2 + (0-1)^2] = x_0^2$$

$$x_0^2 + 6x_0 + 9 + 1 + 9 + 1 = x_0^2$$

$$6x_0 = -20$$

$$x_0 = -\frac{10}{3}.$$

9. (a) $A = \frac{1}{2}(5)(4) = 10$ (b) $A = \frac{1}{2}(5)(6) = 15$

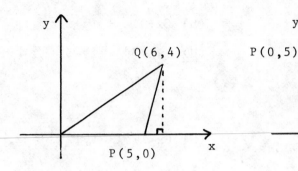 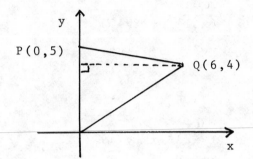

(c) $A = \frac{1}{2}(5)\frac{12}{5} = 6$

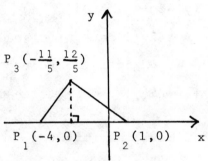

10. 2

11. (a) $A = \frac{1}{2}|a - c||b|$, $P = \sqrt{a^2 + b^2} + \sqrt{b^2 + c^2} + |a - c|$

(b) $A = \frac{1}{8}|a - c||b|$, $P = \frac{1}{2}(\sqrt{a^2 + b^2} + \sqrt{b^2 + c^2} + |a - c|)$

12. (a) 0   (b) $(-1, \frac{9}{2})$ (c) 20   (d) $10\sqrt{5}$

(e) $(x + 1)^2 + (y - \frac{9}{2})^2 = \frac{85}{4}$

SECTION 3.3

1. (a) $\frac{1}{2}$ (b) -4 (c) 0 (d) $\frac{y_0}{x_0}$

   (e) $-\frac{y_0}{x_0}$ (f) -1 (g) 1 (h) 0

2. (a) ℓ_5 (b) ℓ_2 (c) ℓ_3 and ℓ_6

   (d) ℓ_1 and ℓ_3; ℓ_1 and ℓ_6; ℓ_2 and ℓ_5

3. (a) at $(8,0)$ (b) at $(0,4)$ 4. (a) at $(-3,0)$ (b) at $(0,\frac{3}{4})$

5. $a = -\frac{33}{4}$, $b = \frac{15}{7}$ 6. (a) $y_0 = 1$ (b) $y_0 = -\frac{3}{2}$

7. (a) $x_0 = -\frac{7}{3}$ (b) $x_0 = \frac{11}{5}$ 8. at $(a+c, b)$

9.

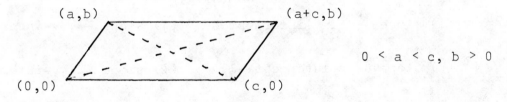

$0 < a < c$, $b > 0$

To correspond to the figure we assume that $0 < a < c$ and $b > 0$.
The length of the slant sides is $\sqrt{a^2 + b^2}$; the length of the horizontal sides is c. We must show that the diagonals are perpendicular if and only if $\sqrt{a^2 + b^2} = c$:

$$\begin{pmatrix} \text{the diagonals are} \\ \text{perpendicular} \end{pmatrix} \leftrightarrow \frac{b}{a+c} \cdot \frac{b}{a-c} = -1$$

$$\leftrightarrow b^2 = -(a^2 - c^2)$$

$$\leftrightarrow a^2 + b^2 = c^2$$

$$\leftrightarrow \sqrt{a^2 + b^2} = c.$$

10. The coordinates of Q satisfy the equation $x^2 + y^2 = r^2$ which we rewrite as

(*) $$x^2 - r^2 = -y^2.$$

(slope of $\overline{PQ}$)(slope of $\overline{RQ}$) = $\left(\dfrac{y}{x+r}\right)\left(\dfrac{y}{x-r}\right) = \dfrac{y^2}{x^2-r^2} = \dfrac{y^2}{-y^2} = -1.$

                                                   by (*)

SECTION 3.4

1. (a) slope 1, y-intercept 4   (b) slope 3, y-intercept -1

    (c) no slope, no y-intercept   (d) slope $\frac{1}{3}$, y-intercept $\frac{2}{3}$
        (the line is vertical)

    (e) slope -1, y-intercept -1   (f) slope 2, y-intercept 3

    (g) slope $-\frac{7}{4}$, y-intercept -1   (h) slope $\frac{7}{4}$, y-intercept 1

    (i) slope $-\dfrac{b}{a}$, y-intercept b   (j) slope $\dfrac{b}{a}$, y-intercept -b

    (k) slope 0, y-intercept $-\frac{5}{2}$ (ℓ) slope $-\frac{3}{2}$, y-intercept $\frac{1}{2}$

2. (a) $y = 5x + 2$ (b) $y = -5x + 2$

    (c) $y = 5x - 2$ (d) $y = -5x - 2$

3. (a) $y = 3$ (b) $y = -3$ 4. (a) $x = 3$ (b) $x = -3$

5. (a) $2x + y - 1 = 0$ (b) $2x + y + 3 = 0$

    (c) $\frac{1}{2}x - y + 1 = 0$ (d) $\frac{1}{2}x - y - 3 = 0$

6. $y = x, \quad y = -x + 1$ 7. $y = \frac{1}{2}x, \quad y = -\frac{1}{2}x$

SECTION 3.5

1. (a) $y - 3 = 5(x - 1)$ (b) $y - 1 = 5(x - 3)$

   (c) $y - 3 = -5(x - 1)$ (d) $y - 1 = -5(x - 3)$

   (e) $y - 3 = 5(x + 1)$ (f) $y + 3 = 5(x - 1)$

   (g) $y + 3 = 5(x + 1)$ (h) $y + 3 = -5(x + 1)$

2. (a) $x + y - 3 = 0$ (b) $2x - y - 4 = 0$

   (c) $3x + y + 1 = 0$ (d) $x + y + 2 = 0$

3. (a) $\dfrac{x}{3} + \dfrac{y}{5} = 1$ (b) $\dfrac{x}{3} - \dfrac{y}{5} = 1$

   (c) $\dfrac{y}{5} - \dfrac{x}{3} = 1$ (d) $\dfrac{x}{3} + \dfrac{y}{5} = -1$

4. (a) $y - 7 = 0$ (b) $x - 2 = 0$ (c) $x + y - 9 = 0$

   (d) $x - y + 5 = 0$ (e) $3x - 2y + 8 = 0$ (f) $2x + 3y - 25 = 0$

5. (a) $y = -2x + 4$ (b) $y - 2 = -2(x - 1)$ (c) $\dfrac{x}{2} + \dfrac{y}{4} = 1$

6. (a) $y - 3 = -\dfrac{1}{4}(x - 3)$ (b) $y = \dfrac{5}{2}$ (c) $x = 4$

   (d) $y - 4 = 3(x + 1)$ (e) $y - \dfrac{b+d}{2} = -\dfrac{c-a}{d-b}\left(x - \dfrac{a+c}{2}\right)$

7. (a) $C = 0$ (b) $B \neq 0$, $-\dfrac{A}{B} = m$ (c) A and B have different signs

   (d) A and B have the same sign (e) $A = 0$, $B \neq 0$

   (f) $B = 0$, $A \neq 0$ (g) $ABC \neq 0$; $\dfrac{C}{A} = -a$ and $\dfrac{C}{B} = -b$

8. $y - 3 = m(x - 1)$, $y - 2 = m(x + 4)$ [The points of trisection are $(1,3)$ and $(-4,2)$.]

9. (a) $y + 2 = 2(x - 3)$, $y + 3 = 2(x - 5)$

(b) $y - \frac{1}{3}b = -\frac{a}{b}(x - \frac{1}{3}a)$, $y - \frac{2}{3}b = -\frac{a}{b}(x - \frac{2}{3}a)$

SECTION 3.6

1. intersect at $(2,-2)$
2. parallel lines
3. intersect at $(3,-4)$
4. intersect at $(-1,-1)$
5. same line
6. intersect at $(\frac{1}{2},2)$
7. parallel lines
8. intersect at $(2,-1)$
9. intersect at $(0,-\frac{1}{2})$
10. intersect at $(\frac{9}{8},4)$
11. $(2,2)$, $(-2,-2)$
12. $(2,-2)$, $(-2,2)$
13. $(2\sqrt{2},0)$
14. $(0,-2\sqrt{2})$
15. does not intersect
16. $(\sqrt{7},1)$, $(-\sqrt{7},1)$
17. $(1+\sqrt{3},1-\sqrt{3})$, $(1-\sqrt{3},1+\sqrt{3})$
18. $(2,2)$
19. (a) $-\frac{5}{12}$ (b) $\frac{5}{12}$
20. (a) $4x + 3y - 6 = 0$ (b) $y - 10 = 0$

(c) $x - 9 = 0$ (d) $3x + 4y - 57 = 0$

21. Suppose that $\ell_1 \parallel \ell_2$. Then either the two lines are vertical or the two lines have the same slope. In the first case, B_1 and B_2 are both zero and

$$A_1 B_2 = A_2 B_1$$

since both sides of the equation are zero. In the second

case

$$-\frac{A_1}{B_1} = \text{slope of } \ell_1 = \text{slope of } \ell_2 = -\frac{A_2}{B_2}.$$

Cross multiplication gives

$$-A_1B_2 = -A_2B_1 \quad \text{and thus} \quad A_1B_2 = A_2B_1.$$

Suppose now that

$$A_1B_2 = A_2B_1.$$

If $B_1 = 0$, then, since $A_1 \neq 0$, $B_2 = 0$. In this case both lines are vertical and hence parallel. If $B_1 \neq 0$, then there are two possibilities. Either $A_2 = 0$, in which case $B_2 \neq 0$ (since A_2 and B_2 cannot both be zero) or $A_2 \neq 0$ in which case again $B_2 \neq 0$, this time because $A_2B_1 \neq 0$. With B_1 and B_2 both different from zero, the equation $A_1B_2 = A_2B_1$ gives

$$-\frac{A_1}{B_1} = -\frac{A_2}{B_2}.$$

The lines are parallel because the slopes are equal.

SECTION 3.7

1. $x = 3, y = 1$

2. $x = 0, y = 4$

3. $x = 2, y = 3$

4. $x = \frac{1}{2}, y = 0$

5. $x = -6, y = 4$

6. $x = \frac{33}{31}, y = -\frac{17}{31}$

7. $x = 1, y = 0, z = 1$

8. $x = 1, y = -2, z = -2$

9. $x = 0, y = 1, z = 2$

10. $x = 2, y = 2, z = 2$

11. $x = 1, y = -1, z = 2$

12. $x = -\frac{43}{6}, y = -\frac{130}{3}, z = -\frac{389}{9}$

13. $x = 1, y = 2, z = 1, w = 2$

14. $x = 2, y = 0, z = 1, w = 1$

15. $x = 0, y = 1, z = 0, w = 2$

16. $x = 2, y = 0, z = 1, w = -1$

SECTION 3.8

1. (a) (i) $(7,-7)$ (ii) $(-7,7)$ (iii) $(-7,-7)$

    (b) (i) $(\sqrt{2},-\sqrt{3})$ (ii) $(-\sqrt{2},\sqrt{3})$ (iii) $(-\sqrt{2},-\sqrt{3})$

    (c) (i) $(-1,0)$ (ii) $(1,0)$ (iii) $(1,0)$

    (d) (i) $(1,1)$ (ii) $(-1,-1)$ (iii) $(-1,1)$

    (e) (i) $(-3,4)$ (ii) $(3,-4)$ (iii) $(3,4)$

    (f) (i) $(0,d)$ (ii) $(0,-d)$ (iii) $(0,d)$

    (g) (i) $(\frac{1}{3},\frac{1}{5})$ (ii) $(-\frac{1}{3},-\frac{1}{5})$ (iii) $(-\frac{1}{3},\frac{1}{5})$

    (h) (i) $(a-b,-a-b)$ (ii) $(b-a,a+b)$ (iii) $(b-a,-a-b)$

2. (a) $(\frac{1}{2},\frac{1}{2})$ (b) 0 (c) $(2\sqrt{2},\sqrt{2})$ (d) $(-\frac{3}{4},\frac{5}{4})$

3. $P_2\,(2-a,4-b)$

4. (a) 2 (b) 2 (c) $2\sqrt{2}$ (d) 13

5. $(0,\sqrt{3})$, $(0,-\sqrt{3})$ 6. (a) $\sqrt{3}$ (b) 1 (c) 0

7. (a) $x - y + 5 = 0$ (b) $2x + y - 5 = 0$ (c) $x - 3y + 15 = 0$

    (d) $x + y - 5 = 0$ (e) $\sqrt{3}x - y + 5 = 0$

8. (a) $x + y - 2a = 0$ (b) $\sqrt{3}x - y = 0$ (c) $3x + y - 6 = 0$

    (d) $10x - 9y - 6 = 0$

9. (a) $x + y - 1 - \sqrt{3} = 0$ (b) $x + \sqrt{3}y - 4 = 0$

    (c) $x + \sqrt{3}y - 4 = 0$

10. (a) $1, -1$ (b) $-\sqrt{2}/2, \sqrt{2}/2$ (c) $\sqrt{3}/2, -\sqrt{3}/2$ (d) 0

11. (a) $(x + 2)^2 + (y - 2)^2 = 2$ (b) $x^2 + y^2 = a^2 + b^2$

12. (a) center at $(3,4)$, $r = 5$ (b) center at $(-2,0)$, $r = 1$

13. (a) $(-1,2)$ (b) parallel   (c) $(\frac{13}{2},\frac{1}{6})$

(d) $(\dfrac{2\sqrt{3} - \sqrt{2}}{5}, \dfrac{2\sqrt{2} + \sqrt{3}}{5})$

14. (a) $x = 2$, $y = 1$, $z = -1$ (b) $x = 2$, $y = 0$, $z = 2$

(c) $x = 2$, $y = 3$, $z = 0$, $w = 2$ (d) $x = 1$, $y = 1$, $z = 0$, $w = 0$

15. $x = 7$ 16. at $(\frac{5}{3},\frac{10}{3})$

17. they are equal: with a, b, c as in the figure, both sums reduce to $2a^2 + 2b^2 + 2c^2$

18. $b = 7$, $A = \frac{25}{2}$ 19. $(-\frac{7}{2},3)$, $(\frac{25}{2},-9)$

20. $\dfrac{x}{a} + \dfrac{y}{a} = 1$

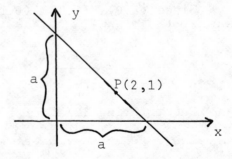

Since $P(2,1)$ lies on the line,

$\dfrac{2}{a} + \dfrac{1}{a} = 1$ and thus $a = 3$.

The equation is $\dfrac{x}{3} + \dfrac{y}{3} = 1$.

21. (a) $(7,5)$, $(7,-3)$ (b) $(4,6)$

(c) no intersection   (d) $(7,5)$, $(0,4)$

(e) $(7,5)$ (f) $(2 + \frac{1}{2}\sqrt{34}, \ 3 + \frac{1}{2}\sqrt{34})$,

$(2 - \frac{1}{2}\sqrt{34}, \ 3 - \frac{1}{2}\sqrt{34})$

22. (a) $9x^2 - y^2 = 0$

$(3x + y)(3x - y) = 0$

so that

$y = -3x$ or $y = 3x$

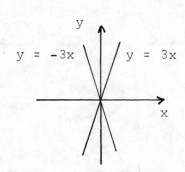

(b) $x^2 - 9y^2 = 0$

$(x + 3y)(x - 3y) = 0$

so that

$y = -\frac{1}{3}x$ or $y = \frac{1}{3}x$

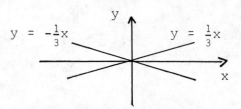

23. Since the area is 6,

$ab = 12$

and

$b = \dfrac{12}{a}$.

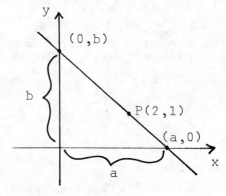

Since $(a,0)$, $(2,1)$, $(0,b)$ are collinear,

$$\frac{b - 1}{0 - 2} = \frac{1}{2 - a}.$$

Substituting $12/a$ for b in the last equation, we get

$$a^2 - 12a + 24 = 0$$

and therefore

$a = 6 + 2\sqrt{3}$ or $a = 6 - 2\sqrt{3}$.

The corresponding values of b are

$b = 3 - \sqrt{3}$ and $b = 3 + \sqrt{3}$.

The lines we want are

$$\frac{x}{6 + 2\sqrt{3}} + \frac{y}{3 - \sqrt{3}} = 1 \quad \text{and} \quad \frac{x}{6 - 2\sqrt{3}} + \frac{y}{3 + \sqrt{3}} = 1.$$

24. The perpendicular bisector of $\overline{PQ}$ is the y-axis:

$$x = 0.$$

The perpendicular bisector of $\overline{PR}$ is the line

$$y - \tfrac{1}{2}c = \frac{a - b}{c}\left[x - \tfrac{1}{2}(a + b)\right].$$

The perpendicular bisector of $\overline{QR}$ is the line

$$y - \tfrac{1}{2}c = \frac{-a - b}{c}\left[x - \tfrac{1}{2}(-a + b)\right].$$

The three lines meet at the point

$$\left(0, \frac{b^2 - a^2 + c^2}{2c}\right).$$

25. On the line $y = x + \dfrac{2A}{|b - a|}$ or on the line $y = x - \dfrac{2A}{|b - a|}$:

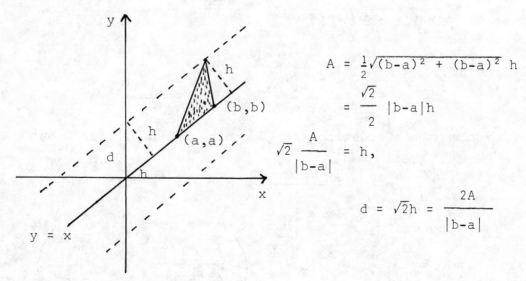

$$A = \tfrac{1}{2}\sqrt{(b-a)^2 + (b-a)^2}\, h$$

$$= \frac{\sqrt{2}}{2}|b-a|h$$

$$\sqrt{2}\,\frac{A}{|b-a|} = h,$$

$$d = \sqrt{2}h = \frac{2A}{|b-a|}$$

26.
$$\left(\frac{x_1 + rx_2}{1 + r}, \frac{y_1 + ry_2}{1 + r} \right):$$

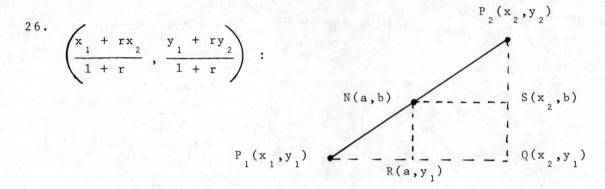

As in the figure, let a be the x-coordinate of R and b the y-coordinate of S. We know that

$$\frac{\text{the length of } \overline{P_1N}}{\text{the length of } \overline{NP_2}} = r.$$

By similar triangles

$$\frac{\text{the length of } \overline{P_1R}}{\text{the length of } \overline{RQ}} = r \quad \text{and} \quad \frac{\text{the length of } \overline{QS}}{\text{the length of } \overline{SP_2}} = r.$$

Thus

$$\frac{a - x_1}{x_2 - a} = r \quad \text{and} \quad \frac{b - y_1}{y_2 - b} = r.$$

Solve these equations for a and b and you'll find that

$$a = \frac{x_1 + rx_2}{1 + r} \quad \text{and} \quad b = \frac{y_1 + ry_2}{1 + r}.$$

27. (a) $Bx - Ay = 0$ (b) $Q = \left(-\frac{AC}{A^2 + B^2}, -\frac{BC}{A^2 + B^2} \right)$

(c) $\frac{|C|}{\sqrt{A^2 + B^2}}$

28.
$$x^2 + y^2 = k^2[(x-a)^2 + y^2]$$

$$= k^2[x^2 - 2ax + a^2 + y^2]$$

$$= k^2x^2 - 2k^2ax + k^2a^2 + k^2y^2$$

$$(1-k^2)x^2 + 2k^2ax + (1-k^2)y^2 = k^2a^2$$

$$x^2 + \frac{2k^2a}{1 - k^2}x + y^2 = \frac{k^2a^2}{1 - k^2}$$

$$x^2 + \frac{2k^2a}{1 - k^2}x + \frac{k^4a^2}{(1-k^2)^2} + y^2 = \frac{k^2a^2}{1 - k^2} + \frac{k^4a^2}{(1 - k^2)^2}$$

$$= \frac{k^2a^2}{(1 - k^2)^2}$$

$$\left(x + \frac{k^2a}{1 - k^2}\right)^2 + y^2 = \frac{k^2a^2}{(1 - k^2)^2}$$

circle centered at $\left(-\dfrac{k^2a}{1 - k^2}, 0\right)$,

radius $\dfrac{ka}{1 - k^2}$

SECTION 4.1

1. $f(0) = 1$, $f(\frac{1}{2}) = \frac{1}{2}$, $f(1) = 0$

2. $f(0) = 1$, $f(\frac{1}{2}) = \frac{1}{2}\sqrt{3}$, $f(1) = 0$

3. $f(0)$ undefined, $f(\frac{1}{2}) = 2$, $f(1) = 1$

4. $f(0) = 2$, $f(\frac{1}{2}) = 4$, $f(1)$ undefined

5. $f(0) = 0$, $f(\frac{1}{2}) = \frac{1}{3}$, $f(1) = \frac{1}{2}$

6. $f(0) = 0$, $f(\frac{1}{2}) = 0$, $f(1) = 0$

7. 0   8. 1 and 3   9. -2   10. $5 \pm 2\sqrt{7}$

11. f does not take on the value 1   12. -1 and 2

13. $f(x-1) = (x-1)^2$, $f(x+1) = (x+1)^2$

14. $f(x-1) = x^2$, $f(x+1) = (x+2)^2$

15. $f(x-1) = (x-1)(x-2)$, $f(x+1) = (x+1)x$

16. $f(x-1) = (x-2)x$, $f(x+1) = x(x+2)$

17. $f(x-1) = \dfrac{x-1}{x}$, $f(x+1) = \dfrac{x+1}{x+2}$

18. $f(x-1) = \dfrac{x-1}{x(x+1)}$, $f(x+1) = \dfrac{x+1}{(x+2)(x+3)}$

19. $\mathrm{dom}(f) = (-\infty, \infty)$, $\mathrm{ran}(f) = [1, \infty)$

20. $\text{dom}(g) = (-\infty, \infty)$, $\quad \text{ran}(g) = [-1, \infty)$

21. $\text{dom}(f) = (-\infty, \infty)$, $\quad \text{ran}(f) = (-\infty, \infty)$

22. $\text{dom}(g) = [0, \infty)$, $\quad \text{ran}(g) = [-1, \infty)$

23. $\text{dom}(f) = (-\infty, 0) \cup (0, \infty)$, $\quad \text{ran}(f) = (0, \infty)$

24. $\text{dom}(g) = (-\infty, 0) \cup (0, \infty)$, $\quad \text{ran}(g) = (-\infty, 0) \cup (0, \infty)$

25. (a) $A(x) = x^2$, $\quad x > 0$ $\qquad$ (b) $A(x) = \frac{1}{2}x^2$, $\quad x > 0$

26. (a) $P(x) = 4x$, $\quad x > 0$ $\qquad$ (b) $P(x) = 2\sqrt{2}x$, $\quad x > 0$

27. $\text{dom}(f) = [1, \infty)$, $\quad \text{ran}(f) = [0, \infty)$

28. $\text{dom}(g) = (-\infty, 1]$, $\quad \text{ran}(g) = [0, \infty)$

29. $\text{dom}(f) = [1, \infty)$, $\quad \text{ran}(f) = [-1, \infty)$

30. $\text{dom}(g) = (-\infty, 1]$, $\quad \text{ran}(g) = [-1, \infty)$

31. $\text{ran}(f) = [-3, \infty)$ $\quad$ since $\quad x^2 + 4x + 1 = (x + 2)^2 - 3$

32. $\text{ran}(g) = [-17, \infty)$ $\quad$ since $\quad x^2 + 8x - 1 = (x + 4)^2 - 17$

33. $\text{ran}(f) = [6, \infty)$ $\quad$ since $\quad x^2 - 6x + 15 = (x - 3)^2 + 6$

34. $\text{ran}(g) = [-23, \infty)$ $\quad$ since $\quad x^2 - 10x + 2 = (x - 5)^2 - 23$

35. $f(x) = \sqrt{1 + x^2}$, $\quad x > 0$ $\qquad$ 36. $f(x) = \sqrt{1 - x^2}$, $\quad 0 < x < 1$

37. (a) dom(f) = [-5,5],   ran(f) = [0,5]   (b) x = ±3

38. (a) dom(g) = (1,∞),   ran(g) = (0,∞)   (b) $x = \frac{26}{25}$

39. (a) dom(f) = $(-\infty, -3-\sqrt{5}]$ U $[-3+\sqrt{5}, \infty)$,   ran(f) = [0,∞)

     (b) x = 0

40. (a) dom(g) = (-∞,∞),   ran(g) = [7,∞)   since

$$g(x) = 2x^2 - 4x + 9$$
$$= 2(x^2 - 2x + 1) + 7$$
$$= 2(x - 1)^2 + 7$$

     (b) $x = 1 \pm \sqrt{2}$

41. (a) $V(x) = \frac{8}{9}\sqrt{3}x^3$,   x > 0   (b) $A(x) = 8x^2$,   x > 0

     (c) $x > 3\sqrt{3}$

SECTION 4.2

1. f(a) = D,   f(b) = 0,   f(c) = A,   f(0) = 0,   f(d) = C,   f(e)=B

2. [a,e]   3.   [A,D]   4.   at b and at 0

5. maximum D taken on at a   6.   minimum A taken on at c

7. increases on [c,d]; decreases on [a,c] and on [d,e]

8. positive on [a,b) and on (0,e]; negative on (b,0)

9. and 10.

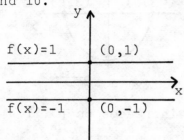

f(x)=1   (0,1)

f(x)=-1   (0,-1)

11. and 12.

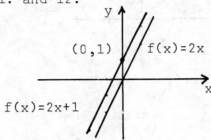

(0,1)   f(x)=2x

f(x)=2x+1

13. and 14.

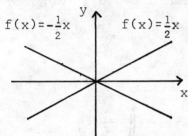

$f(x)=-\frac{1}{2}x$ $f(x)=\frac{1}{2}x$

15. and 16.

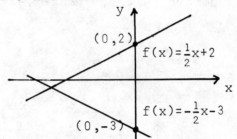

(0,2)

$f(x)=\frac{1}{2}x+2$

$f(x)=-\frac{1}{2}x-3$

(0,-3)

17. (a) If $P(x_1,y_1)$ and $Q(x_1,y_2)$ both lie on the graph of f, then from the coordinates of P we know that $y_1 = f(x_1)$ and from the coordinates of Q we know that $y_2 = f(x_1)$. It follows that $y_1 = y_2$ and therefore P = Q.

(b) curve (c) is not the graph of a function

18.

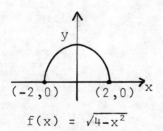

(-2,0)   (2,0)

$f(x) = \sqrt{4-x^2}$

f increases on [-2,0]

f decreases on [0,2]

domain [-2,2]; range [0,2]

19.

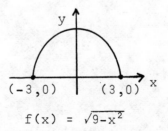

(-3,0)   (3,0)

$f(x) = \sqrt{9-x^2}$

f increases on [-3,0]

f decreases on [0,3]

domain [-3,3]; range [0,3]

20.

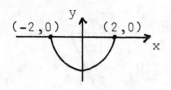

$$f(x) = -\sqrt{4-x^2}$$

f increases on [0,2]

f decreases on [-2,0]

domain [-2,2]; range [-2,0]

21.

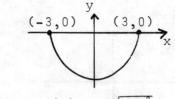

$$f(x) = -\sqrt{9-x^2}$$

f increases on [0,3]

f decreases on [-3,0]

domain [-3,3]; range [-3,0]

22.

x	y
0	0
$\frac{1}{9}$	$\frac{1}{3}$
$\frac{1}{4}$	$\frac{1}{2}$
$\frac{1}{16}$	$\frac{1}{4}$
$\frac{9}{4}$	$\frac{3}{2}$
4	2
9	3

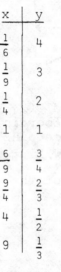

$$f(x) = \sqrt{x}$$

23.

x	y
$\frac{1}{16}$	4
$\frac{1}{9}$	3
$\frac{1}{4}$	2
1	1
$\frac{16}{9}$	$\frac{3}{4}$
$\frac{9}{4}$	$\frac{2}{3}$
4	$\frac{1}{2}$
9	$\frac{1}{3}$

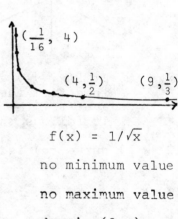

$$f(x) = 1/\sqrt{x}$$

no minimum value

no maximum value

domain $(0,\infty)$

range $(0,\infty)$

24. $(-\infty,1) \cup (1,\infty)$

25. on $(-\infty,-1]$ and $[0,1)$

26. on $(-1,0]$ and $(1,\infty)$

27. no minimum value

28. no maximum value

29. $(-\infty,-1] \cup [0,1)$

30. domain $(-\infty,0) \cup (0,\infty)$

range $(-\infty,0)$

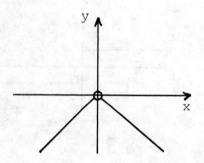

31. domain $(-\infty,\infty)$

range $(-\infty,\infty)$

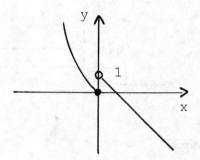

32. domain $(-\infty,\infty)$

range $(-\infty,\infty)$

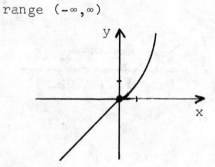

33. domain $(-\infty,\infty)$; range $(0,\infty)$

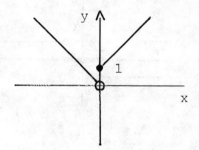

34. domain $[0,\infty)$; range $[1,\infty)$

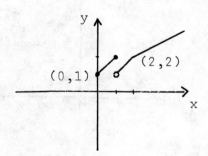

35. domain $(-\infty,0) \cup (0,2) \cup (2,\infty)$

range $\{-1\} \cup (0,\infty)$

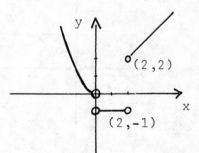

36. domain $(-\infty,0) \cup (0,\infty)$

    range $\{-1,1\}$

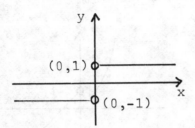

37. domain $(-\infty,0) \cup (0,\infty)$

    range $\{-1,1\}$

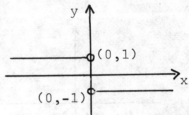

38. domain $(-\infty,\infty)$

    range $\{-1,0,1\}$

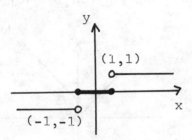

39. domain $[-2,2]$

    range $\{0,1\}$

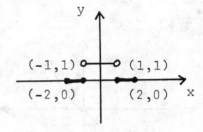

40. domain $(-\infty,\infty)$

    range $\{-2,-1,0,1,2\}$

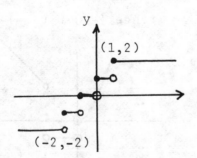

41. domain $[0,5]$

    range $\{1,2,3,4,5\}$

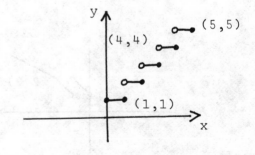

SECTION 4.3

1.

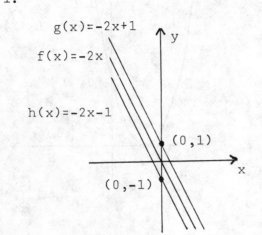

2.

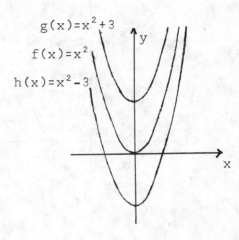

3.

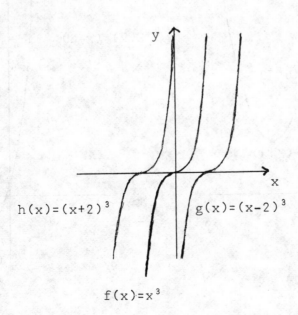

4.

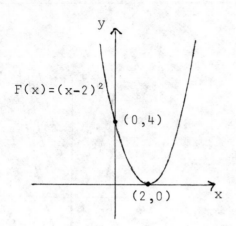

$F(x) = (x-2)^2$

(0,4)

(2,0)

5.

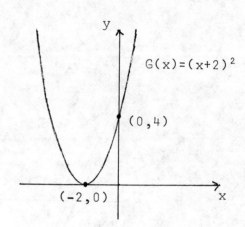

$G(x) = (x+2)^2$

(0,4)

(-2,0)

6.

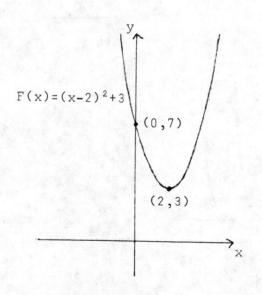

$F(x) = (x-2)^2 + 3$

(0,7)

(2,3)

7.

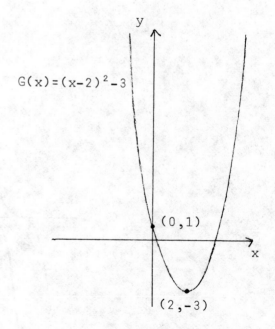

$G(x) = (x-2)^2 - 3$

(0,1)

(2,-3)

8.

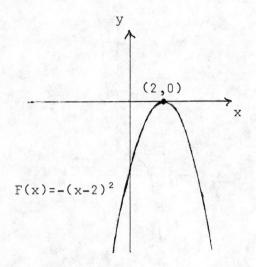

$$F(x)=-(x-2)^2$$

9.

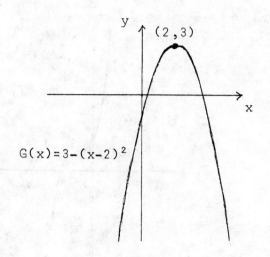

$$G(x)=3-(x-2)^2$$

10.

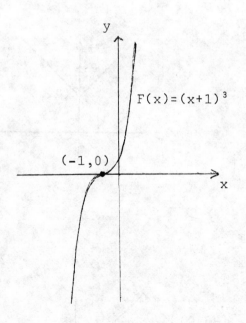

$$F(x)=(x+1)^3$$

11.

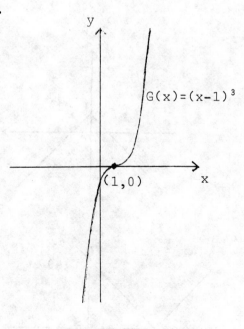

$$G(x)=(x-1)^3$$

12.

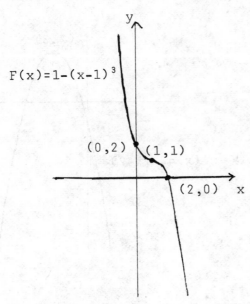

$F(x)=1-(x-1)^3$

$(0,2)$ $(1,1)$

$(2,0)$

13.

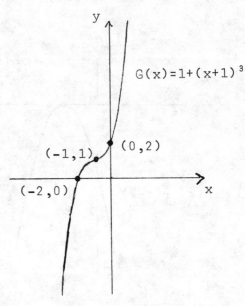

$G(x)=1+(x+1)^3$

$(-1,1)$ $(0,2)$

$(-2,0)$

14.

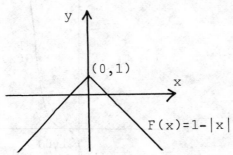

$(0,1)$

$F(x)=1-|x|$

15.

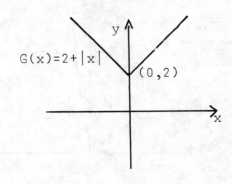

$G(x)=2+|x|$

$(0,2)$

16.

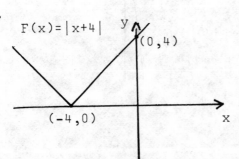

$F(x)=|x+4|$

$(0,4)$

$(-4,0)$

17.

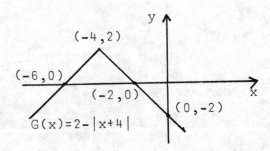

$(-4,2)$

$(-6,0)$

$(-2,0)$

$(0,-2)$

$G(x)=2-|x+4|$

18.

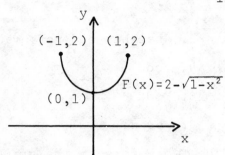

19.

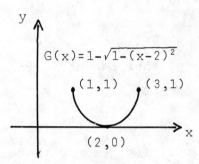

20.

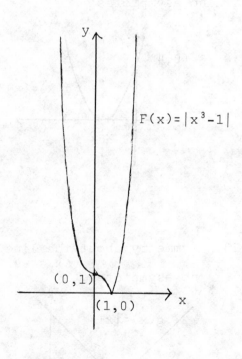

21.

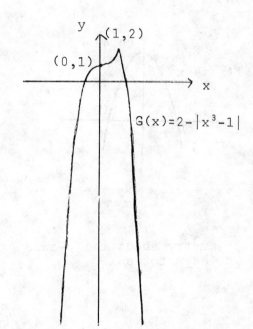

SECTION 4.4

1. even

2. neither odd nor even

3. neither odd nor even

4. odd

5. even

6. odd

7. odd

8. even

9. No; if it were, there would be two points on the graph with the same first coordinate and that can't be.

10. symmetry about the y-axis
    no asymptotes

11. symmetry about the line x = 2
    no asymptotes

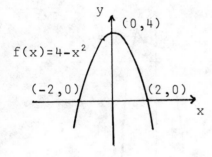

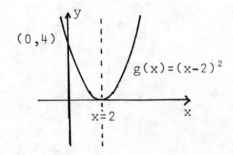

12. symmetry about the y-axis
    no asymptotes

13. symmetry about the line
    x = -4
    no asymptotes

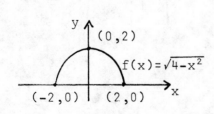

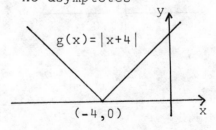

14. symmetry about P(0,1)
    vertical asymptote y-axis
    horizontal asymptote y = 1

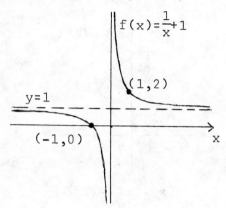

$f(x)=\frac{1}{x}+1$

(1,2)

y=1

(-1,0)

15. symmetry about P(1,0)
    vertical asymptote x = 1
    horizontal asymptote y-axis

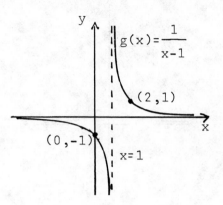

$g(x)=\frac{1}{x-1}$

(2,1)

(0,-1)

x=1

16. symmetric about the y-axis
    vertical asymptote y-axis
    horizontal asymptote y = 1

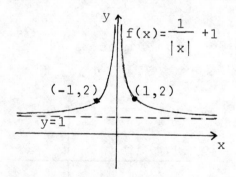

$f(x)=\frac{1}{|x|}+1$

(-1,2)   (1,2)

y=1

17. symmetry about the origin
    no asymptotes

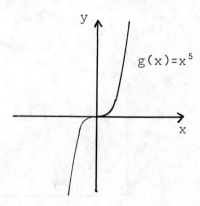

$g(x)=x^5$

18. symmetry about the y-axis
    horizontal asymptote x-axis

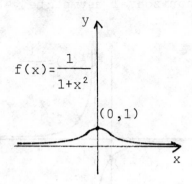

$$f(x) = \frac{1}{1+x^2}$$

(0,1)

19. symmetry about P(1,2)
    no asymptotes

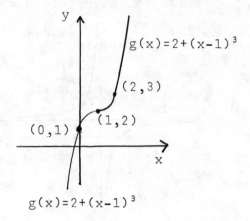

$g(x) = 2 + (x-1)^3$

(2,3)

(0,1) (1,2)

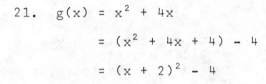

$g(x) = 2 + (x-1)^3$

20. $f(x) = x^2 - 6x + 10$

   $= (x^2 - 6x + 9) + 1$

   $= (x - 3)^2 + 1$

   symmetry about the line
   $x = 3$
   no asymptotes

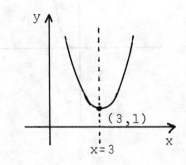

(3,1)

x = 3

21. $g(x) = x^2 + 4x$

   $= (x^2 + 4x + 4) - 4$

   $= (x + 2)^2 - 4$

   symmetry about the line
   $x = -2$
   no asymptotes

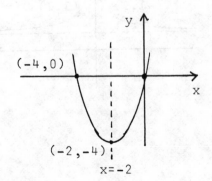

(-4,0)

(-2,-4)

x = -2

22. symmetry about P(2,0)
    vertical asymptote x = 2
    horizontal asymptote x-axis

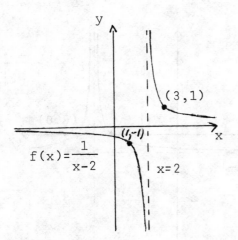

$f(x) = \dfrac{1}{x-2}$ (3,1)   (1,-1)   x=2

23. symmetry about the line
                           x = 2
    vertical asymptote x = 2
    horizontal asymptote x-axis

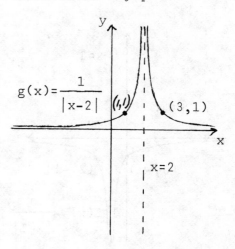

$g(x) = \dfrac{1}{|x-2|}$ (1,1)   (3,1)   x=2

24. symmetry about P(2,-1)
    vertical asymptote x = 2
    horizontal asymptote y = -1

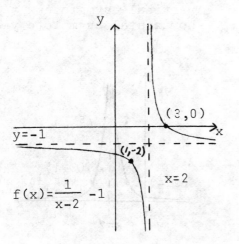

y=-1   (3,0)   (1,-2)   x=2 $f(x) = \dfrac{1}{x-2} - 1$

25. symmetry about P(3,2)
    vertical asymptote x = 3
    horizontal asymptote y = 2

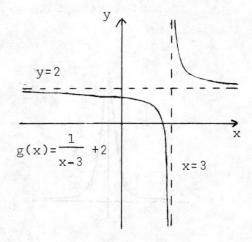

y=2 $g(x) = \dfrac{1}{x-3} + 2$ x=3

26. symmetry about the line
                    x = 1
    vertical asymptote x = 1
    horizontal asymptote x-axis

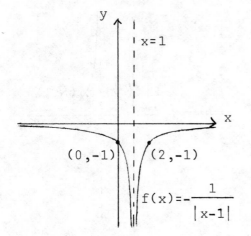

$$f(x) = -\frac{1}{|x-1|}$$

27. symmetry about the line
                    x = 5
    vertical asymptote x = 5
    horizontal asymptote y = -1

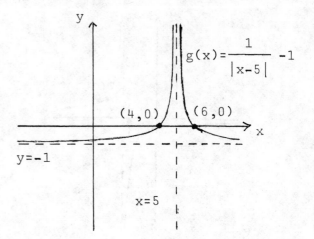

$$g(x) = \frac{1}{|x-5|} - 1$$

28. symmetry about the y-axis
    vertical asymptote y-axis
    horizontal asymptote x-axis

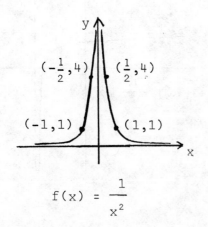

$$f(x) = \frac{1}{x^2}$$

29. symmetry about the line
                    x = 2
    vertical asymptote x = 2
    horizontal asymptote y-axis

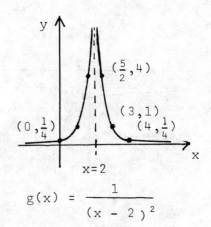

$$g(x) = \frac{1}{(x-2)^2}$$

30. symmetry about the line
                    x = -1
    vertical asymptote x = -1
    horizontal asymptote y = -2

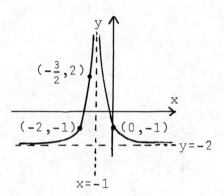

$$f(x) = \frac{1}{(x+1)^2} - 2$$

31. symmetry about the origin
    vertical asymptote y-axis
    horizontal asymptote x-axis

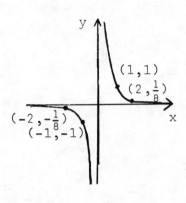

$$g(x) = \frac{1}{x^3}$$

32. symmetry about P(2,0)
    vertical symptote x = 2
    horizontal asymptote x-axis

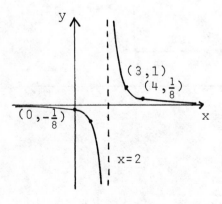

$$f(x) = \frac{1}{(x-2)^3}$$

33. symmetry about the line
                    x = 1
    vertical asymptote x = 1
    horizontal asymptote y = 2

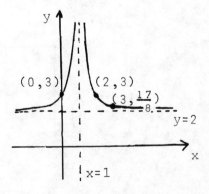

$$g(x) = \frac{1}{|x-1|^3} + 2$$

34. $g(x) = \frac{1}{2}[f(-x) + f(-(-x))]$, $h(-x) = \frac{1}{2}[f(-x) - f(-(-x))]$

$\qquad\quad = \frac{1}{2}[f(-x) + f(x)]$ $\qquad\qquad\qquad = \frac{1}{2}[f(-x) - f(x)]$

$\qquad\quad = \frac{1}{2}[f(x) + f(-x)]$ $\qquad\qquad\qquad = -\frac{1}{2}[f(x) - f(-x)]$

$\qquad\quad = g(x)$ $\qquad\qquad\qquad\qquad\; = -h(x).$

35. $f(a - x)$

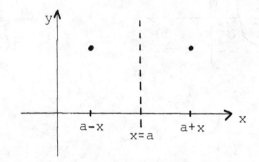

36. $b - f(a - x)$

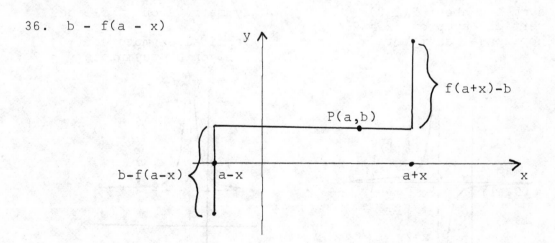

SECTION 4.5

1. (a) $(f+g)(x) = 2x^2$ (b) $(f-g)(x) = -2a^2$

   (c) $(fg)(x) = x^4 - a^4$ (d) $\left(\dfrac{f}{g}\right)(x) = \dfrac{x^2 - a^2}{x^2 + a^2}$

2. (a) $(3f-2g)(x) = 23x - 11$ (b) $(4f+5g)(x) = 23x^2 + 16$

   (c) $(4f+g)(x) = 11x^2 + 16x$

3. (a) $(6f+3g)(x) = 9\sqrt{x}$ $(x>0)$ (b) $(fg)(x) = x - \dfrac{2}{x} + 1$ $(x>0)$

   (c) $\left(\dfrac{f}{g}\right)(x) = \dfrac{x - 1}{x + 2}$ $(x>0)$

4. We can write

$$f(x) = \begin{cases} x, & x \leq 0 \\ -1, & 0 < x < 1 \\ -1, & x \geq 1 \end{cases} \text{ and } g(x) = \begin{cases} -x, & x \leq 0 \\ -x, & 0 < x < 1 \\ x^2, & x \geq 1 \end{cases}.$$

   (a) $(f+g)(x) = \begin{cases} 0, & x \leq 0 \\ -1 - x, & 0 < x < 1 \\ -1 + x^2, & x \geq 1 \end{cases}$

   (b) $(f-g)(x) = \begin{cases} 2x, & x \leq 0 \\ -1 + x, & 0 < x < 1 \\ -1 - x^2, & x \geq 1 \end{cases}$

   (c) $(fg)(x) = \begin{cases} -x^2, & x \leq 0 \\ x, & 0 < x < 1 \\ -x^2, & x \geq 1 \end{cases}$

5. (a) $(f+g)(x) = \begin{cases} 1 - x, & x \leq 1 \\ 2x - 1, & 1 < x < 2 \\ 2x - 2, & x \geq 2 \end{cases}$

(b) $(f-g)(x) = \begin{cases} 1-x, & x \leq 1 \\ 2x-1, & 1 < x < 1 \\ 2x, & x \geq 2 \end{cases}$ (c) $(fg)(x) = \begin{cases} 0, & x < 2 \\ 1-2x, & x \geq 2 \end{cases}$

Figure 4.5.1

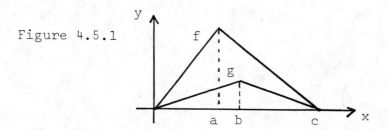

6.

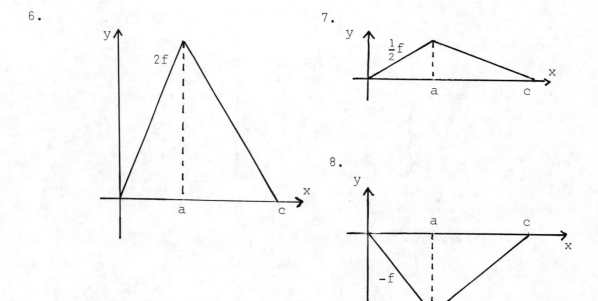

7.

8.

9.

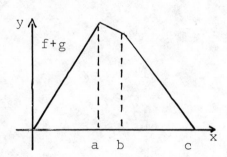

10.

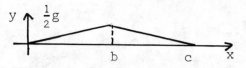

11.

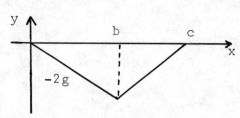

12.

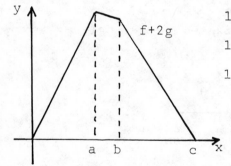

13.

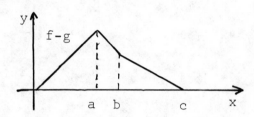

14.

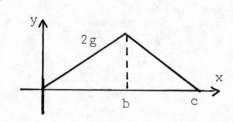

15. even

16. even

17. odd

18. $f(x) = g(x) + h(x)$ with

$g(x) = \frac{1}{2}[f(x) + f(-x)]$ and $h(x) = \frac{1}{2}[f(x) - f(-x)]$

SECTION 4.6

1. $2x^2 + 5$ 2. $(2x + 5)^2$ 3. $\sqrt{x^2 + 5}$

4. $x + \sqrt{x}$ 5. x with $x \neq 0$ 6. $\dfrac{1}{(x - 1)^2}$

7. $\dfrac{1}{x} - 1$ 8. $x^2(x - 1)^2 - 1$ 9. $\dfrac{1}{x^2 + 1}$

10. $x^2 - \dfrac{x^2}{1 + x^2}$ with $x \neq 0$ 11. $4x^2 - 4$

12. $4x^2 - 1$ 13. $(x^4 - 1)^2$ 14. $16x^2 - 1$

15. $2x^2 + 1$ 16. $2x^2 + 2$ 17. $g(x) = x^2$

18. $g(x) = x^3$ 19. $g(x) = (x - 1)^2$ 20. $g(x) = 1 + x^3$

21. $g(x) = x^2$ 22. $g(x) = 2x^3 - 1$ 23. $g(x) = a^2x^2,\ x \neq 0$

24. $g(x) = x - 2$: $x^2 - 4x + 4 = (x - 2)^2$

25. $g(x) = ax,\ x \neq 0$: $\dfrac{ax}{a^2x^2 - 1} = \dfrac{1}{ax - \dfrac{1}{ax}}$ for $x \neq 0$

26. $f(x) = ax + b$ 27. $f(x) = \sqrt{x^2 + 1}$

28. $f(x) = (x^2 - 1)^3$ 29. $f(x) = x(x^2 + 1)$

30. $f(x) = \sqrt{x}$ 31. $f(x) = x\sqrt{x}$

32. $f(x) = \dfrac{1}{(x + 5)^5}$ 33. $f(x) = \dfrac{3x}{x^2 + 1}$

34. $f(x) = \dfrac{x}{(x^2 + 1)^2}$ 35. $f(x) = \dfrac{1 - \sqrt{x}}{1 + \sqrt{x}}$

SECTION 4.7

1. 12

2. 125

3. $\dfrac{1}{125}$

4. $\dfrac{1}{10}$

5. 10

6. $\dfrac{1}{10}$

7. $-\dfrac{1}{2}$

8. $\dfrac{1}{5}$

9. 25

10. $\dfrac{1}{25}$

11. $\dfrac{1}{32}$

12. $-\dfrac{1}{243}$

13. 144

14. 18

15. 10

16. 10

17. 2

18. 6

19. $\dfrac{26}{3}$

20. 8

21. $\dfrac{1}{8}$

22. $\dfrac{9}{28}$

23. $\dfrac{3}{4}$

24. $\dfrac{1}{44}$

25. 46

26. 162

27. 5.98×10^{1}

28. 5.98×10^{3}

29. 5.98×10^{-1}

30. 5.98×10^{-3}

31. 3×10^{-5}

32. 1.28×10^{5}

33. 1.2×10^{-3}

34. 1.7×10^{-4}

35. x^{4}/y^{6}

36. x^{6}/y^{9}

37. $4a^{2}b^{3}$

38. $32y$

39. ac/b^{2}

40. 16

41. ab

42. $\dfrac{2}{3}y^{2} + \dfrac{1}{3}$

43. $-\dfrac{1}{xy}$

44. $\dfrac{1}{x^{2}} + \dfrac{1}{y^{2}}$

45. $\dfrac{8y^{2}}{25x^{7}}$

46. $\dfrac{1}{24x^{5}y^{7}}$

47. $\dfrac{1}{x(1 - x)}$

48. $\dfrac{x^{2}}{x - 1}$

49. $a + b$

50. $a - b$

51. $a - 1$

52. 1

53. $\dfrac{a^{2}}{5a - 3}$

54. $a - a^{2}$

55. $\dfrac{x^{4}}{x^{6} + 1}$

56. $\dfrac{1}{(x^{2} + 1)^{2}(x - 1)^{2}}$

57. $\dfrac{x^{2}}{x^{2} + x + 1}$

58. $\dfrac{x^2 - 1}{x^2 - x + 1}$ 59. $\dfrac{uv}{v - u}$ 60. $\dfrac{a - b}{ab}$

61. $x = 9$ 62. $x = \dfrac{4}{9}$ 63. $x = \dfrac{1}{9}$ 64. $x = 25$

65. $x = 4$:

$$(\sqrt{x} + \sqrt{x + 5})^2 = 25$$
$$x + 2\sqrt{x}\sqrt{x + 5} + x + 5 = 25$$
$$2\sqrt{x}\sqrt{x + 5} + 2x + 5 = 25$$
$$2\sqrt{x}\sqrt{x + 5} = 20 - 2x$$
$$\sqrt{x}\sqrt{x + 5} = 10 - x$$
$$x(x + 5) = 100 - 20x + x^2$$
$$x^2 + 5x = 100 - 20x + x^2$$
$$25x = 100$$
$$x = 4$$

66. $x = 7$ 67. $x = 5$ 68. $x = 11$

SECTION 4.8

1. $f^{-1}(x) = \dfrac{1}{5}(x - 3)$ 2. $f^{-1}(x) = \dfrac{1}{3}(x - 5)$

3. $f^{-1}(x) = \dfrac{1}{4}(x + 7)$ 4. $f^{-1}(x) = \dfrac{1}{7}(x + 4)$

5. not one-to-one   6. $f^{-1}(x) = x^{\frac{1}{5}}$

7. $f^{-1}(x) = (x - 1)^{\frac{1}{5}}$ 8. not one-to-one

9. $f^{-1}(x) = [\dfrac{1}{3}(x - 1)]^{\frac{1}{3}}$ 10. $f^{-1}(x) = (x + 1)^{\frac{1}{3}}$

11. $f^{-1}(x) = 1 - x^{\frac{1}{3}}$

12. not one-to-one

13. $f^{-1}(x) = (x - 2)^{\frac{1}{3}} - 1$

14. $f^{-1}(x) = \frac{1}{4}(x^{\frac{1}{3}} + 1)$

15. $f^{-1}(x) = x^{\frac{5}{3}}$

16. $f^{-1}(x) = (1 - x)^3 + 2$

17. $f^{-1}(x) = \frac{1}{3}(2 - x^{\frac{1}{3}})$

18. not one-to-one

19. $f^{-1}(x) = \frac{1}{4}[1 + (x + 5)^3]$

20. $f^{-1}(x) = \frac{1}{4}[(x + 3)^{\frac{1}{5}} - 1]$

21. not one-to-one

22. $f^{-1}(x) = [(x - 2)^{\frac{1}{3}} - 1]^{\frac{1}{5}}$

23. $f^{-1}(x) = \frac{1}{x}$

24. $f^{-1}(x) = 1 - \frac{1}{x}$

25. not one-to-one

26. not one-to-one

27. $f^{-1}(x) = (\frac{1}{x} - 1)^{\frac{1}{3}}$

28. $f^{-1}(x) = \frac{x}{1 + x}$

29. $f^{-1}(x) = \frac{2 - x}{x - 1}$

30. $f^{-1}(x) = \frac{1 + 3x}{2 - x}$

31. f

32.

$h(x) = x^2, \quad x \geq 0$

$g(x) = \sqrt{x}$

33.

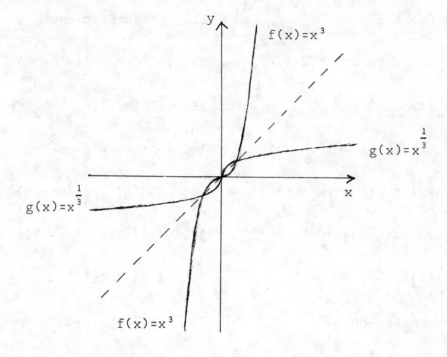

34. $f(x_1) = f(x_2) \quad \leftrightarrow \quad ax_1^2 + bx_1 + c = ax_2^2 + bx_2 + c$

$$\leftrightarrow \quad a(x_1^2 - x_2^2) + b(x_1 - x_2) = 0$$

$$\leftrightarrow \quad (x_1 - x_2)[a(x_1 + x_2) + b] = 0$$

$$\leftrightarrow \quad x_1 = x_2 \quad or \quad x_1 + x_2 = -\frac{b}{a} .$$

The function is not one-to-one because it takes on the same
value at any two numbers that add up to -b/a.

35. (a)   (b)   (c)

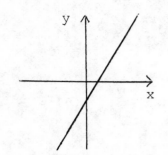 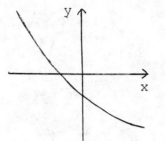 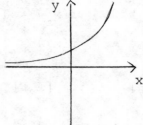

36. no; $f(x) = x^3 - x$ is odd but not one-to-one since $f(0) = f(1)$

37. (a) $f(g(x_1)) = f(g(x_2)) \rightarrow g(x_1) = g(x_2) \rightarrow x_1 = x_2$.

   (b) $(f \circ g)((f \circ g)^{-1}(x)) = x$, $g((f \circ g)^{-1}(x)) = f^{-1}(x)$

   $(f \circ g)^{-1}(x) = g^{-1}(f^{-1}(x))$, $(f \circ g)^{-1} = g^{-1} \circ f^{-1}$

38. $f(f^{-1}(-x)) = -x = -f(f^{-1}(x)) = f(-f^{-1}(x))$.

   f is odd

   Since f is one-to-one,

$$f^{-1}(-x) = -f^{-1}(x),$$

   which shows that f is odd.

39. take $f(x) = x$, $g(x) = -x$

40. take $f(x) = x$, $g(x) = -x$

SECTION 4.9

1. $f(x_1) = C$, $f(x_2) = 0$, $f(x_3) = D$, $f(x_4) = 0$,

   $f(x_5) = A$, $f(x_6) = 0$, $f(x_7) = E$

2. $[x_1, x_7]$ 3. $[A, E]$ 4. at x_2, x_4, x_6 5. $f(0) = B$

6. f is positive on (x_2, x_4) and $(x_6, x_7]$

   f is negative on $[x_1, x_2)$ and (x_4, x_6)

7. f increases on $[x_1, x_3]$ and on $[x_5, x_7]$; f decreases on $[x_3, x_5]$

8. maximum value is E; taken on at x_7

9. minimum value is A; taken on at x_5

10. $(-\infty, \infty)$ 11. $[-2, \infty)$ $[f(x) = (x+1)^2 - 2]$

12. no maximum value   13. minimum value is -2

14. -1 15. at $x = -1 - \sqrt{2}$ and $x = -1 + \sqrt{2}$

16. f is positive on $(-\infty, -1-\sqrt{2})$ and $(-1+\sqrt{2}, \infty)$

17. f is negative on $(-1-\sqrt{2}, -1+\sqrt{2})$

18. the graph of f is the graph of g displaced one unit to the left, two units down

19. the graph is symmetric about the line $x = -1$

20.

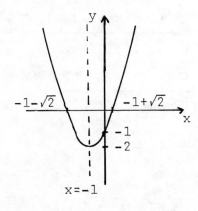

21. $\dfrac{125}{4}$ 22. 10   23. $-\dfrac{1}{10}$

24. 25   25. 110

26. $\dfrac{1}{2}$; $32^{-\frac{1}{4}} \cdot 8^{\frac{1}{12}} = 2^{-\frac{5}{4}} \cdot 2^{\frac{1}{4}}$

$= 2^{-1} = \dfrac{1}{2}$

27. -1;

$(2^{\frac{1}{2}} + 3^{\frac{1}{2}})(2^{\frac{1}{2}} - 3^{\frac{1}{2}}) = 2 - 3$

$= -1$

28. $\dfrac{1}{6}$; $(2^{-\frac{1}{2}} + 3^{-\frac{1}{2}})(2^{-\frac{1}{2}} - 3^{-\frac{1}{2}}) = 2^{-1} - 3^{-1} = \dfrac{1}{2} - \dfrac{1}{3} = \dfrac{1}{6}$

29. 23   30. $\dfrac{341}{324}$ 31. 1.07×10^5

32. 4.88×10^3 33. 4.45×10^{-2} 34. 1.07×10^6

35. 4.88×10^{-3} 36. 4.45×10^8 37. $\dfrac{x^6}{y^4}$ 38. $\dfrac{y^6}{4x^4}$

39. $\dfrac{2}{xy^2}$ 40. $\dfrac{a^2}{b^5}$ 41. $\dfrac{a^6}{b^2}$ 42. $\dfrac{1}{ab^3c^5d^3}$

43. $\dfrac{x}{x^2 + 1}$;   multiply numerator and denominator by $x^{\frac{5}{2}}$

44. $\dfrac{ax}{1 + a^2x^2}$;   multiply numerator and denominator by $(ax)^{\frac{1}{2}}$

45. $1 + a^2$; $\dfrac{\sqrt[4]{a^2} + \sqrt[4]{a^{10}}}{\sqrt{a}} = \dfrac{a^{\frac{1}{2}} + a^{\frac{5}{2}}}{a^{\frac{1}{2}}} = 1 + a^2$

46. a^2;   the expression reduces to $\dfrac{a \cdot a \cdot a}{a}$

47. $\dfrac{x^2 + 1}{x^2 - x + 1}$; $\dfrac{(1 + x^{-1})(1 - x^{-4})}{(1 - x^{-2})(1 + x^{-3})} = \dfrac{(1 + x^{-1})(1 - x^{-4})}{(1 - x^{-2})(1 + x^{-3})} \cdot \dfrac{x^5}{x^5}$

$$= \frac{(x + 1)(x^4 - 1)}{(x^2 - 1)(x^3 + 1)}$$

$$= \frac{x^2 + 1}{x^2 - x + 1}$$

48. -1 ; $\left(\dfrac{a^{-1} + b^{-1}}{a^{-1} - b^{-1}}\right)^3 \left(\dfrac{a + b}{a - b}\right)^{-3} = \left(\dfrac{b + a}{b - a}\right)^3 \left(\dfrac{a - b}{a + b}\right)^3 = -1$

49. $\dfrac{1}{x^4}$; $\dfrac{(1 + x^{-1})^2 (1 - x^{-1})^2}{(x^2 - 1)^2} = \dfrac{(1 - x^{-2})^2}{(x^2 - 1)^2} = \left(\dfrac{1 - x^{-2}}{x^2 - 1}\right)^2$

$$= \left(\frac{x^2 - 1}{x^2 - 1}\right)^2 \frac{1}{x^4} = \frac{1}{x^4}$$

50. $\dfrac{(x + a^4)(x^4 + a)}{(x^2 + a^3)(x^3 + a^2)}$;

$$\frac{(a^{-4} + x^{-1})(a^{-1} + x^{-4})}{(a^{-3} + x^{-2})(a^{-2} + x^{-3})} = \frac{(a^{-4} + x^{-1})(a^{-1} + x^{-4})}{(a^{-3} + x^{-2})(a^{-2} + x^{-3})} \cdot \frac{a^5 x^5}{a^5 x^5}$$

$$= \frac{(a^{-4} + x^{-1})(a^4 x) \cdot (a^{-1} + x^{-4})(ax^4)}{(a^{-3} + x^{-2})(a^3 x^2) \cdot (a^{-2} + x^{-3})(a^2 x^3)}$$

$$= \frac{(x + a^4)(x^4 + a)}{(x^2 + a^3)(x^3 + a^2)}$$

51.

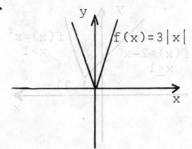

$f(x)=3|x|$

52.

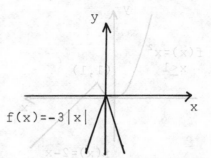

$f(x)=-3|x|$

53.

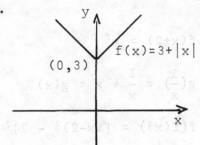

$(0,3)$

$f(x)=3+|x|$

54.

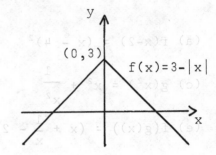

$(0,3)$

$f(x)=3-|x|$

55.

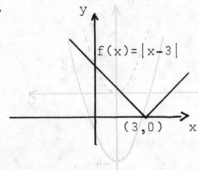

$f(x)=|x-3|$

$(3,0)$

56.

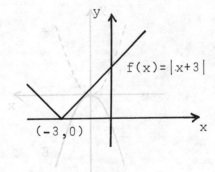

$f(x)=|x+3|$

$(-3,0)$

57.

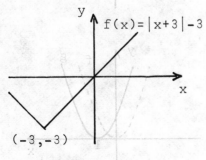

$f(x)=|x+3|-3$

$(-3,-3)$

58.

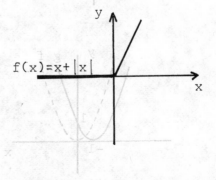

$f(x)=x+|x|$

59.

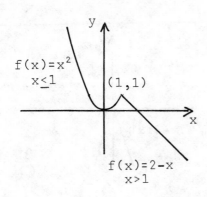

$f(x)=x^2$
  $x\leq1$

(1,1)

$f(x)=2-x$
  $x>1$

60.

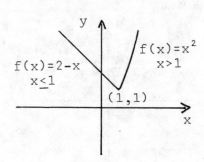

$f(x)=2-x$
  $x\leq1$

$f(x)=x^2$
  $x>1$

(1,1)

61. (a) $f(x-2) = (x - 4)^2$

(b) $f(x+2) = x^2$

(c) $g(x^2) = x^2 + \dfrac{1}{x^2}$

(d) $g\left(\dfrac{1}{x}\right) = \dfrac{1}{x} + x = g(x)$

(e) $f\bigl(g(x)\bigr) = \left(x + \dfrac{1}{x} - 2\right)^2$

(f) $f\bigl(f(x)\bigr) = \left[(x-2)^2 - 2\right]^2$

62.

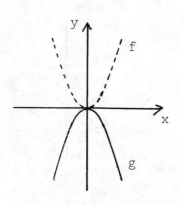

63.

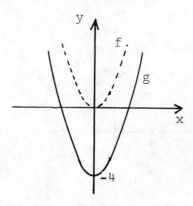

64.

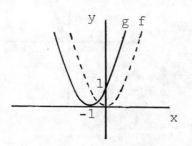

65.

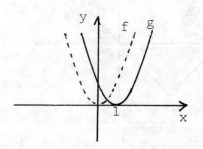

66.
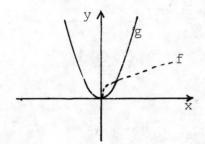

67.
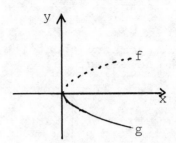

68.
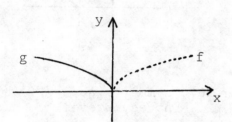

69.
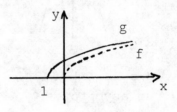

70.
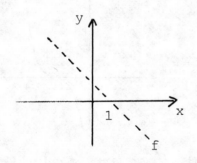

71.
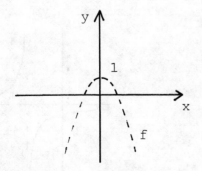

72. even   73. even   74. neither   75. even   76. odd

77. symmetry about the y-axis
    no asymptotes

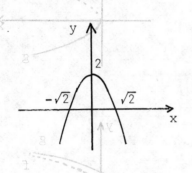

78. symmetry about the line x=2
    no asymptotes

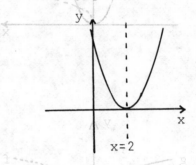

79. symmetry about P(0,2)
    no asymptotes

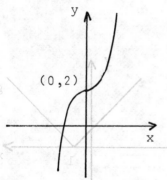

80. symmetry about P(2,0)
    no asymptotes

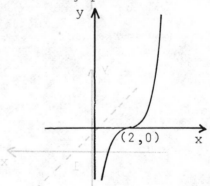

81. symmetry about P(-1,0)
    vertical asymptote x = -1
    horizontal asymptote x-axis

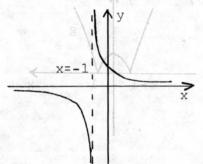

82. symmetry about P(2,0)
    vertical asymptote x = 2
    horizontal asymptote x-axis

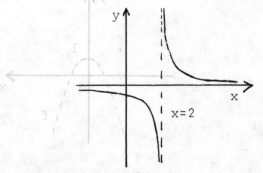

83. symmetry about P(1,2)
     vertical asymptote x = 1
     horizontal asymptote y = 2

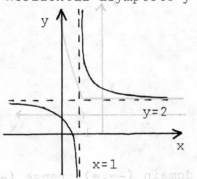

84. symmetry about P(-2,-1)
     vertical asymptote x = -2
     horizontal asymptote y = -1

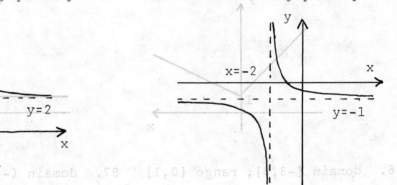

85. $f(f^{-1}(x)) = x,$ $\quad 1 - [f^{-1}(x)]^3 = x,$ $\quad [f^{-1}(x)]^3 = 1 - x$

$f^{-1}(x) = (1 - x)^{\frac{1}{3}}$

86. $f(f^{-1}(x)) = x,$ $\quad 3[f^{-1}(x)]^{\frac{1}{5}} = x,$ $\quad f^{-1}(x) = \left(\frac{x}{3}\right)^5$

87. $f(f^{-1}(x)) = x,$ $\quad \dfrac{2}{f^{-1}(x)} - 1 = x,$ $\quad f^{-1}(x) = \dfrac{2}{1 + x}$

88. $f^{-1}(x) = x^3 - 1$

89. $f^{-1}(x) = (1 - x^{\frac{1}{5}})^3$

90. not one-to-one

91. not one-to-one

92. $f^{-1}(x) = \dfrac{x}{2 - x}$

93. $f^{-1}(x) = \dfrac{x}{1 - 2x}$

94. domain $(-\infty,\infty)$; range $[1,\infty)$ 95. domain $(-\infty,\infty)$; range $[1,\infty)$

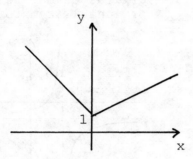   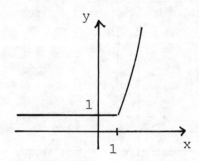

96. domain $[-3,3]$; range $[0,1]$ 97. domain $(-\infty,\infty)$; range $(-\infty,1]$

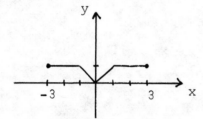   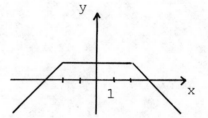

98. (a) $(f+g)(x) = \begin{cases} 2 - x, & x \le 0 \\ 2 + \frac{1}{2}x, & 0 < x \le 1 \\ 1 + \frac{1}{2}x + x^2, & x > 1 \end{cases}$

(b) $(f-g)(x) = \begin{cases} -x, & x \le 0 \\ \frac{1}{2}x, & 0 < x \le 1 \\ 1 + \frac{1}{2}x - x^2, & x > 1 \end{cases}$

(c) $(fg)(x) = \begin{cases} 1 - x, & x \le 0 \\ 1 + \frac{1}{2}x, & 0 < x \le 1 \\ x^2 + \frac{1}{2}x^3, & x > 1 \end{cases}$

99. $(f \circ g)(-x) = f(g(-x)) = f(g(x)) = (f \circ g)(x).$

100. (a) $f(x) = (x - 1)^{\frac{1}{3}}$ (b) $f(x) = (x + 1)^{\frac{1}{3}}$

(c) $f(x) = (x + 2)^{\frac{1}{3}} + 1$ (d) $f(x) = (x - 2)^{\frac{1}{3}} - 1$

(e) $f(x) = -x^{\frac{1}{3}}$

Figure 4.9.2

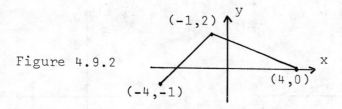

101.

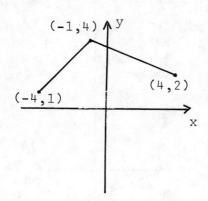

102.

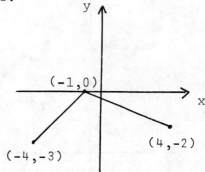

103.

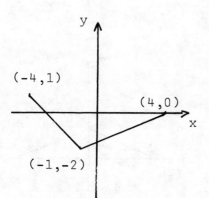

104.

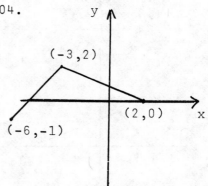

105.

106.

107.

108.

109.

110.

111.

112.

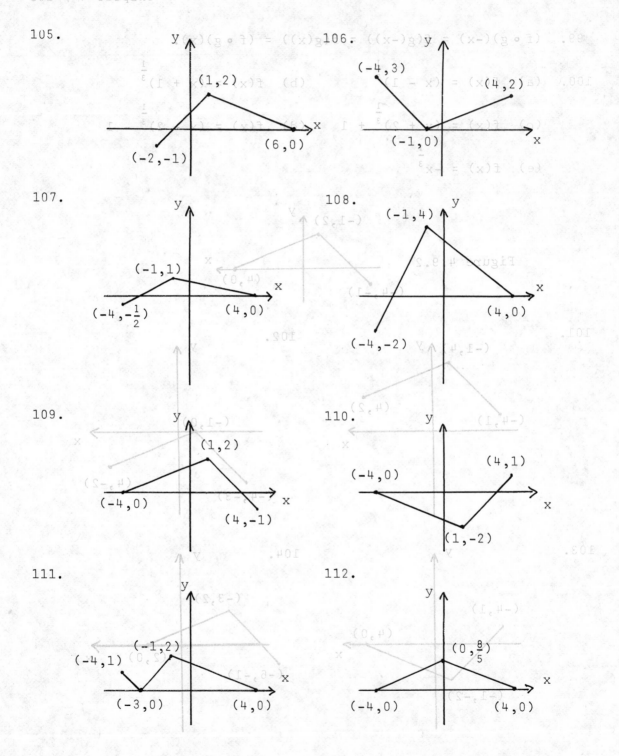

113. (a) $f(x_1) = f(x_2) \rightarrow \dfrac{ax_1 + b}{cx_1 + d} = \dfrac{ax_2 + b}{cx_2 + d}$

$\rightarrow (ax_1 + b)(cx_2 + d) = (cx_1 + d)(ax_2 + b)$

$\rightarrow \cancel{acx_1x_2} + adx_1 + bcx_2 + \cancel{bd} = \cancel{acx_1x_2} +$

$bcx_1 + adx_2 + \cancel{bd}$

$\rightarrow adx_1 + bcx_2 = bcx_1 + adx_2$

$\rightarrow (ad - bc)x_1 = (ad - bc)x_2$

$\rightarrow x_1 = x_2$ provided that $ad - bc \neq 0$.

(b) $f^{-1}(x) = \dfrac{b - dx}{cx - a}$

114. (a)　　　　　　　　　　(b)

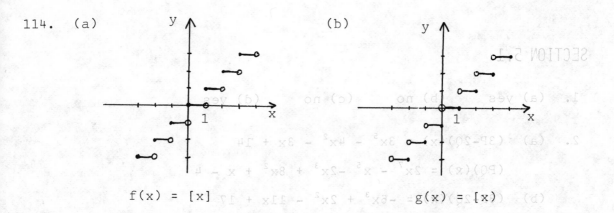

$f(x) = [x]$　　　　　　　$g(x) = [x]$

115.

	f_1	f_2	f_3	f_4	f_5	f_6
f_1	f_1	f_2	f_3	f_4	f_5	f_6
f_2	f_2	f_1	f_4	f_3	f_6	f_5
f_3	f_3	f_5	f_1	f_6	f_2	f_4
f_4	f_4	f_6	f_2	f_5	f_1	f_3
f_5	f_5	f_3	f_6	f_1	f_4	f_2
f_6	f_6	f_4	f_5	f_2	f_3	f_1

116.   (a) m = 2x + h;

$$m = \frac{(x + h)^2 - x^2}{(x + h) - x} = \frac{x^2 + 2xh + h^2 - x^2}{h} = 2x + h$$

(b) as h tends to zero, m tends to 2x

117.   (a) m = $3x^2 + 3xh + h^2$;

$$m = \frac{(x + h)^3 - x^3}{(x + h) - x} = \frac{x^3 + 3x^2h + 3xh^2 + h^3 - x^3}{h}$$

$$= 3x^2 + 3xh + h^2$$

(b) as h tends to zero, m tends to $3x^2$

SECTION 5.1

1.   (a) yes   (b) no   (c) no   (d) yes

2.   (a) $(3P-2Q)(x) = 3x^5 - 4x^2 - 3x + 14$

   $(PQ)(x) = 2x^7 - x^5 - 2x^3 + 8x^2 + x - 4$

(b) $(3P-2Q)(x) = -6x^3 + 2x^2 - 11x + 17$

   $(PQ)(x) = 6x^5 - 5x^4 + 11x^3 + 5x^2 + 8x - 5$

3.   (a) 1   (b) 0   (c) 8   (d) 6   (e) 5   (f) 9

4.   (a) yes   (b) yes   (c) no   (d) yes

5.   mn

6. Suppose that the polynomial had $n+1$ distinct roots:

$$c_1, c_2, \ldots, c_{n+1}.$$

Then the product

$$(x - c_1)(x - c_2) \cdots (x - c_{n+1}),$$

which has degree $n+1$, would be a factor of the polynomial. This is impossible. By (5.1.2), a polynomial of degree n cannot have a factor of degree $n+1$.

7. $n - k + 1$

8. (a) $P(x) = (x - 1)(x^2 + 5x + 4) = x^3 + 4x^2 - x - 4$

(b) $P(x) = (x - 2)(x - 3)(x + 2) = x^3 - 3x^2 - 4x + 12$

(c) $P(x) = (x + 2)(x + 1)x^2 = x^4 + 3x^3 + 2x^2$

(d) $P(x) = (x + 2)(x + 1)(x - 1)(x - 2) = x^4 - 5x^2 + 4$

(e) $P(x) = x(x^2 - 3)(x + \frac{3}{2}) = x^4 + \frac{3}{2}x^3 - 3x^2 - \frac{9}{2}x$

9. (a) 1, 2, 3   (b) -1, -2, -3   (c) 1, -2, 3

(d) 1   (e) 1, -1   (f) $-\frac{1}{2}$, $\frac{1}{3}$, $-\frac{5}{4}$

10. (a) 1 and 2 are simple roots, 3 is a double root

(b) -1 and 1 are both double roots

(c) $-\frac{5}{2}$ is a root of multiplicity 4

(d) -1, $\frac{2}{3}$, 1 are all simple roots

(e) -1 is a double root, 1 is a root of multiplicity 4

(f) -3 is a double root, -2 is a simple root, -1 is a triple root

(g) -2 is a simple root, 0 is a root of multiplicity 4, -1 and 1 are both double roots

11. (a) -1, 0, 2 are simple roots

    (b) 1 is a double root, 2 is a simple root

    (c) -2 and 1 are both double roots

    (d) $-\sqrt{2}$ is a simple root, 1 is a double root, $\sqrt{2}$ is a simple root

    (e) $-\frac{1}{2}$ and 3 are double roots

    (f) $-\frac{1}{2}\sqrt{2}$, 0, $\frac{1}{2}\sqrt{2}$ are simple roots

SECTION 5.2

1. $x^2 - 3x - 1$, remainder 2 2. $x^2 + 4x - 4$, remainder 3

3. $x^2 - 2x + 4$ 4. $3x^3 + 2x^2 + 4x + 10$, remainder 21

5. $x^3 - 2x^2 - 4x - 22$, remainder -60

6. $3x^3 + 5x^2 + 11x + 26$

7. $x^4 - 2x^3 + 2x^2 - 3x + 6$, remainder -13

8. $2x^4 - x^3 - 3x^2 - 8x - 7$ 9. $P(-2) = -105$, $P(\frac{1}{2}) = 0$

10. $P(\frac{2}{3}) = 0$, $P(3) = 490$ 11. $P(-2) = -62$, $P(-\frac{2}{3}) = 26$

12. $P(4) = 39$, $P(3) = 89$ 13. $P(\frac{1}{2}) = 0$, $P(\frac{1}{5}) = 0$

14. $P(-\frac{1}{2}) = 50$, $P(-3) = 3445$ 15. 1 and $\pm\sqrt{5}$ are simple roots

16. -1 is a simple root

17. $\frac{1}{2}$ is a double root, $\frac{1}{3}$ is a simple root

18. $-\frac{1}{3}$ is a simple root

19. 4 is a simple root, $-\frac{1}{2}$ is a double root

20. $-\frac{1}{3}$ is a triple root

21. $\pm\frac{1}{2}$ and $\pm\sqrt{2}$ are simple roots

22. -2 and -3 are simple roots

23. -1 and 2 are simple roots, 3 is a double root

24. -1 is a triple root, $-\frac{2}{3}$ is a simple root

25. -1 and -2 are simple roots, $\frac{2}{5}$ is a double root

26. 0 is a double root; $\frac{1}{2}$, $\frac{1}{3}$, $\frac{1}{4}$ are simple roots

27. -2 is a double root

28. 1 is a simple root, $\frac{1}{2}$ is a double root

29. (a) x = 3 ft   (b) $\frac{1}{2}$ ft

Solution for (a): The volume being 60 cubic feet, we know that

$$x(x + 1)(x + 2) = 60.$$

This equation simplifies to

$$x^3 + 3x^2 + 2x - 60 = 0.$$

The only real value of x that satisfies this equation is x=3.

30.   r = 4 ft

Solution: the equation looks like this

$$\frac{1}{3}\pi r^2 (2r + 1) = 48\pi.$$

This simplifies to

$$2r^3 + r^2 - 144 = 0.$$

The only real root of this equation is r = 4.

SECTION 5.3

1.   (a) (1,2), (3,∞)   (b) (-∞,1), (2,3)

2.   (a) (-∞,1), (3,∞)   (b) (1,2), (2,3)

3.   (a) (-∞,1), (1,2), (3,∞)   (b) (2,3)

4.   (a) (1,2), (2,3), (3,∞)   (b) (-∞,1)

5.   (a) (2,3), (3,∞)   (b) (-∞,1), (1,2)

6.   (a) (-∞,1), (2,3), (3,∞)   (b) (1,2)

7.   roots $-\frac{3}{2}$, -1, 1
     (a) $(-\frac{3}{2},-1)$, (1,∞)   (b) $(-\infty,-\frac{3}{2})$, (-1,1)

8.   only root -5   (a) (-5,∞)   (b) (-∞,-5)

9.   roots 0, 1, 2
     (a) (1,2)   (b) (-∞,0), (0,1), (2,∞)

10. roots -6, -2, 0, 2

    (a) $(-\infty,-6)$, $(-2,0)$, $(2,\infty)$ (b) $(-6,-2)$, $(0,2)$

11. roots $-\frac{1}{2}$, 2   (a) $(-\frac{1}{2},2)$, $(2,\infty)$ (b) $(-\infty,-\frac{1}{2})$

12. roots $-\frac{1}{2}$, 1, 2

    (a) $(-\infty,-\frac{1}{2})$, $(1,2)$ (b) $(-\frac{1}{2},1)$, $(2,\infty)$

13. roots -1, 1   (a) $(-\infty,-1)$, $(1,\infty)$ (b) $(-1,1)$

14. roots -1, $-\frac{1}{3}$, $\frac{1}{3}$, $\frac{1}{2}$

    (a) $(-\infty,-1)$, $(-\frac{1}{3},\frac{1}{3})$, $(\frac{1}{2},\infty)$ (b) $(-1,-\frac{1}{3})$, $(\frac{1}{3},\frac{1}{2})$

15. roots -2, $-\sqrt{2}$, 1, $\sqrt{2}$, 2

    (a) $(-2,-\sqrt{2})$, $(1,\sqrt{2})$, $(2,\infty)$ (b) $(-\infty,-2)$, $(-\sqrt{2},1)$, $(\sqrt{2},2)$

16. roots -2, $-\frac{1}{2}$, $\frac{1}{2}$, 2, 3

    (a) $(-2,-\frac{1}{2})$, $(\frac{1}{2},2)$, $(3,\infty)$ (b) $(-\infty,-2)$, $(-\frac{1}{2},\frac{1}{2})$, $(2,3)$

17. roots 1, 2

    (a) $(2,\infty)$ (b) $(-\infty,1)$, $(1,2)$

18. roots 1, 2, 3

    (a) $(-\infty,1)$, $(1,2)$, $(2,3)$, $(3,\infty)$

    (b) the function is negative nowhere

SECTION 5.4

1. $1 - 4x + 6x^2 - 4x^3 + x^4$ 2. $1 - 5x + 10x^2 - 10x^3 + 5x^4 - x^5$

3. $16 - 32x + 24x^2 - 8x^3 + x^4$ 4. $81 + 216x + 216x^2 + 96x^3 + 16x^4$

5. $\frac{1}{64}x^6 - \frac{3}{16}x^5y + \frac{15}{16}x^4y^2 - \frac{5}{2}x^3y^3 + \frac{15}{4}x^2y^4 - 3xy^5 + y^6$

6. $\frac{1}{32}x^5 + \frac{5}{8}x^4y^2 + 5x^3y^4 + 20x^2y^6 + 40xy^8 + 32y^{10}$

7. $243x^{10} - 135x^8y + 30x^6y^2 - \frac{10}{3}x^4y^3 + \frac{5}{27}x^2y^4 - \frac{1}{243}y^5$

8. $x^{20} - 10x^{16}y + 40x^{12}y^2 - 80x^8y^3 + 80x^4y^4 - 32y^5$

9. $64x^{24} - 192x^{20} + 240x^{16} - 160x^{12} + 60x^8 - 12x^4 + 1$

10. $2(1 + 10x^2 + 5x^4)$ 11. $2(1 + 15x^2 + 15x^4 + x^6)$

12. $2\left[5a^3 + 10\left(\frac{1}{a}\right) + \left(\frac{1}{a}\right)^5\right]$ 13. $2\left[6\frac{a^5}{b^4c} + 20\frac{a^3}{c^3} + 6\frac{ab^4}{c^5}\right]$

14. 56 15. -56 16. 220 17. -792

18. 1365 19. 5005 20. 216 21. -27

22. $-\frac{5}{4}$ 23. -40 24. $\frac{25}{16}$ 25. -330

26. 45 27. $\frac{35}{8}$

28. $\binom{n}{k} = \frac{n(n-1)\cdots(n-k+1)}{k!} = \frac{n(n-1)\cdots(n-k+1)}{k!} \cdot \frac{(n-k)!}{(n-k)!} = \frac{n!}{k!(n-k)!}$

29. $\binom{n}{0} = \dfrac{n!}{0!n!} = 1, \qquad \binom{n}{n} = \dfrac{n!}{n!0!} = 1$

30. $\binom{n}{k} = \dfrac{n!}{k!(n-k)!} = \dfrac{n!}{(n-k)!k!} = \dfrac{n!}{(n-k)!\,[n-(n-k)]!} = \binom{n}{n-k}$

31. $\binom{n-1}{k-1} + \binom{n-1}{k} = \dfrac{(n-1)!}{(k-1)!(n-k)!} + \dfrac{n-1)!}{k!(n-1-k)!}$

$$= (n-1)! \left[\dfrac{k + (n-k)}{k!(n-k)!} \right]$$

$$= (n-1)! \left[\dfrac{n}{k!(n-k)!} \right] = \dfrac{n!}{k!(n-k)!} = \binom{n}{k}$$

32. $k\binom{n}{k} + (k+1)\binom{n}{k+1} = k \left[\dfrac{n!}{k!(n-k)!} \right] + (k+1) \left[\dfrac{n!}{(k+1)!(n-k-1)!} \right]$

$$= n! \left[\dfrac{k + (n-k)}{k!(n-k)!} \right]$$

$$= n! \left[\dfrac{n}{k!(n-k)!} \right]$$

$$= n \left[\dfrac{n!}{k!(n-k)!} \right] = n\binom{n}{k}$$

SECTION 5.5

1. (a) $800:   5000(1.16) - 5000 = 800

   (b) about $832: $5000(1.08)^2 - 5000 \cong 832$

   (c) about $850: $5000(1.04)^4 - 5000 \cong 849.50$

   (d) about $859: $5000(1.02)^8 - 5000 \cong 858.50$

2. (a) $6000:   10,000(1.60) - 10,000 = 6000

   (b) about $7623: $10,000(1.12)^5 - 10,000 \cong 7623$

   (c) about $8061: $10,000(1.03)^{20} - 10,000 \cong 8061$

3. 10% compounded semiannually: $(1.05)^2 = 1.1025 > 1.1$

4. 8% compounded quarterly: $(1.02)^4 = 1.0824 > 1.08$

5. about 26.8%: $(1.02)^{12} \cong 1.2682$

6. (a) about 9 years   (b) a little more than 6 years

7. (a) about $9526: $12,000(1.08)^{-3} \cong 12,000(0.7938) = 9525.60$

   (b) about $9484: $12,000(1.04)^{-6} \cong 12,000(0.7903) = 9483.60$

   (c) about $9462: $12,000(1.02)^{-12} = 12,000(0.7885) = 9462.00$

8. (a) about $4500: $4000(1.04)^3 \cong 4000(1.1249) = 4499.60$

   (b) about $5039: $4000(1.08)^3 \cong 4000(1.2597) = 5038.80$

   (c) about $5620: $4000(1.12)^3 = 4000(1.4049) = 5619.60$

9. (a) about $17,784: $24,000(1.03)^{-10} \cong 24,000(0.7410) = 17,784$

   (b) about $16,214: $24,000(1.04)^{-10} \cong 24000(0.6756) = 16,214.40$

   (c) about $14,734: $24,000(1.05)^{-10} \cong 24000(0.6139) = 14,733.60$

SECTION 5.6

1. a^2

2. a

3. $\dfrac{1}{a^2}$

4. $27^{\sqrt{2}}$

5. $3^{\sqrt{2}}$

6. $\dfrac{1}{3}$

7. $\dfrac{2^4}{a^4}$

8. $x^2 - y^2$

9. 75

10. 9

11. $\dfrac{1}{16}$

12. $\dfrac{1}{10}$

13. $\dfrac{1}{3}$

14. 3

15. 3

16. $\dfrac{8a^{\frac{9}{2}}}{b^6}$

17. 11

18. $\dfrac{1}{5}$

19. b

20. b^{18}

21. $(0,\infty)$

22. $(-\infty,0)$

23. $(-\infty,0)$

24. $(-\infty,-2)$

25. $(3,\infty)$

26. $(-\infty,0)$

27. $(0,\infty)$

28. $(-\infty,1)$

29. $(-\infty,-2)$

30. $x = 1$

31. $x = 2$

32. $x = -3$

33. $x = 0$

34. all real x

35. $x = \dfrac{1}{5}$

36. $x = \dfrac{1}{10}$

37. $x = -\dfrac{1}{9}$

38. $x = \dfrac{1}{7}(2\sqrt{2} - 1)$

39. Figure 5.6.1

40. by reflection in the y-axis

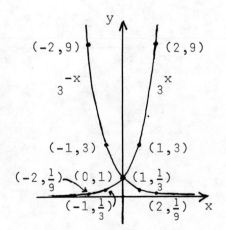

Figure 5.6.1

41.

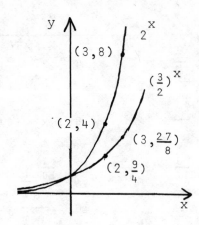

42.

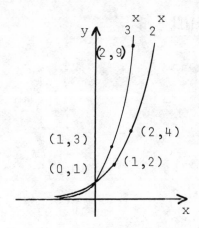

43.

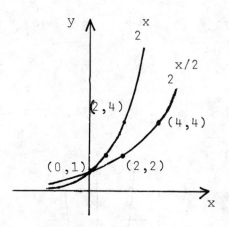

44.

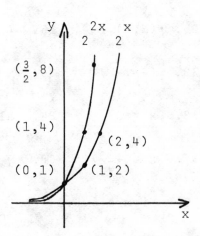

45.

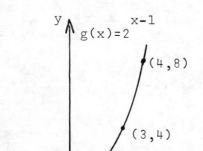

the graph of g is the graph
of $f(x) = 2^x$ displaced one
unit to the right

46.

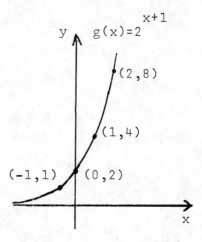

the graph of g is the graph
of $f(x) = 2^x$ displaced one
unit to the left

47.

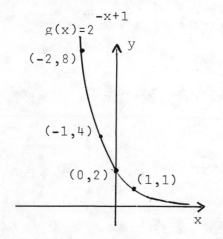

the graph of g is the graph
of $f(x) = 2^{-x}$ displaced one
unit to the right:

$$g(x) = f(x-1)$$

48.

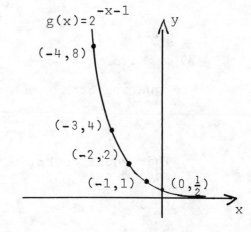

the graph of g is the graph
of $f(x) = 2^{-x}$ displaced one
unit to the left:

$$g(x) = f(x+1)$$

49. No; that implication is valid only if $b > 1$; if $b < 1$, then
$$r_1 < z < r_2 \rightarrow b^{r_2} < b^z < b^{r_1}.$$

50. $10^{\sqrt{2}}$: $10^{\sqrt{2}} = 10 \cdot 10^{\sqrt{2}-1} > 10 > \sqrt{10}$

$\quad\quad$ └ since $\sqrt{2}-1 > 0$

51. $(\sqrt{5})^{10}$: $10^{\sqrt{5}} < 10^{\sqrt{9}} = 10^3 = 1000$;

$\quad\quad (\sqrt{5})^{10} = 5^5 = (625)(5) > 1000$

52. $2^{\sqrt{2}}$: $2^{\sqrt{2}} > 2^1 = (\sqrt{2})^2$

53. $3^{\sqrt{3}}$: $3^{\sqrt{3}} = (\sqrt{3})^{2\sqrt{3}} > (\sqrt{3})^3$

$\quad\quad$ └ since $2\sqrt{3} > 3$

54. $(\sqrt{5})^5$: $5^{\sqrt{5}} = (\sqrt{5})^{2\sqrt{5}} < (\sqrt{5})^5$

$\quad\quad$ └ since $2\sqrt{5} < 5$ as you can tell
$\quad\quad\quad$ by squaring both sides

55. (a) $x = 1$ or $x = 4$:

Squaring both sides of $x^{\sqrt{x}} = (\sqrt{x})^x$, we have

$$x^{2\sqrt{x}} = x^x.$$

This equation holds if $x = 1$ or if $2\sqrt{x} = x$. In the second case $x = 4$.

(b) $(0,1) \cup (4,\infty)$:

$$x^{\sqrt{x}} < (\sqrt{x})^x \leftrightarrow x^{2\sqrt{x}} < x^x.$$

For $x > 1$

$$x^{2\sqrt{x}} < x^x \leftrightarrow 2\sqrt{x} < x \leftrightarrow 2 < \sqrt{x} \leftrightarrow 4 < x.$$

For $0 < x < 1$

$$x^{2\sqrt{x}} < x^x \leftrightarrow x < 2\sqrt{x} \leftrightarrow \sqrt{x} < 2.$$

This last equation certainly holds if $0 < x < 1$.

(c) $(1,4)$

56. $x = 1, \sqrt{27}$ 57. $x = 1, n^{\frac{n}{n-1}}$

SECTION 5.7

1. -1 2. 3 3. -3 4. -5 5. $\frac{9}{2}$ 6. 6

7. $\frac{2}{3}$ 8. $\frac{1}{4}$ 9. $-\frac{2}{5}$ 10. $-\frac{8}{5}$ 11. $\frac{5}{3}$ 12. $-\frac{3}{4}$

13. -1 14. $-\frac{2}{5}$ 15. $\frac{1}{2}$ 16. $\frac{1}{2}$ 17. $\frac{1}{3}$ 18. $\frac{1}{6}$

19. 2.1761: $\log_{10} 150 = \log_{10} 3 \cdot 5 \cdot 10 = \log_{10} 3 + \log_{10} 5 + 1$
$$\cong 0.4771 + 0.6990 + 1 = 2.1761$$

20. 0.1761: $\log_{10} 1.5 = \log_{10} \dfrac{3 \cdot 5}{10} = \log_{10} 3 + \log_{10} 5 - 1$
$$\cong 0.4771 + 0.6990 - 1 = 0.1761$$

21. 3.8751: $\log_{10} 7500 = \log_{10} 3 \cdot 5^2 \cdot 10^2 = \log_{10} 3 + 2 \log_{10} 5 + 2$
$$\cong 0.4771 + 2(0.6990) + 2$$
$$= 3.8751$$

22. -0.1249: $\log_{10} 0.75 = \log_{10} 3 \cdot 5^2 \cdot 10^{-2} = \log_{10} 3 + 2 \log_{10} 5 - 2$
$$\cong -0.1249$$

23. -2.3189: $\log_{10} \dfrac{3}{625} = \log_{10} 3 \cdot 5^{-4} = \log_{10} 3 - 4 \log_{10} 5$

$$\cong 0.4771 - 4(0.6990)$$

$$= -2.3189$$

24. -0.3329: $\log_{10} \sqrt{\dfrac{27}{125}} = \log_{10} (3^3 \cdot 5^{-3})^{\frac{1}{2}}$

$$= \tfrac{1}{2}(3 \log_{10} 3 - 3 \log_{10} 5)$$

$$\cong \tfrac{1}{2}[3(0.4771) - 3(0.6990)] \cong -0.3329$$

25. -0.7823: $\log_{10} (0.0045)^{\frac{1}{3}} = \log_{10} (3^2 \cdot 5 \cdot 10^{-4})^{\frac{1}{3}}$

$$= \tfrac{1}{3}(2 \log_{10} 3 + \log_{10} 5 - 4)$$

$$\cong \tfrac{1}{3}[2(0.4771) + 0.6990 - 4] \cong -0.7823$$

26. 8.1303: $\log_{10} 135,000,000 = \log_{10} (3^3 \cdot 5 \cdot 10^6)$

$$= 3 \log_{10} 3 + \log_{10} 5 + 6$$

$$\cong 3(0.4771) + 0.6990 + 6 = 8.1303$$

27. 0.4690: $\log_{10} (\sqrt[3]{0.3} \ \sqrt[5]{0.5})^2 = 2[\log_{10} (3 \cdot 10^{-1})^{\frac{1}{3}} + \log_{10} (5 \cdot 10^{-1})^{\frac{1}{5}}]$

$$= 2[\tfrac{1}{3}(\log_{10} 3 - 1) + \tfrac{1}{5}(\log_{10} 5 - 1)]$$

$$\cong 2[\tfrac{1}{3}(0.4771) - 1) + \tfrac{1}{5}(0.6990 - 1)]$$

$$= 0.4690$$

28. $A + 2 + 3C$ 29. $-A - 1 - C$ 30. $\tfrac{1}{2}(A + 1 + C)$

31. $4(3A + 2 + C)$ 32. $\tfrac{1}{2}(A + 1) - 2C$ 33. $\tfrac{1}{3}(2 - A - C)$

34. $C - \tfrac{1}{2}(A + 1)$ 35. $\tfrac{1}{2}(A - 3 - 3C)$ 36. $2(\tfrac{2}{3}A - \tfrac{3}{4} - \tfrac{4}{5}C)$

37. $a + b + c$ 38. $(a + b + c)A$ 39. $b(A + C)$

40. $aA + b + cC$

41. $cA + a + bC$

42. $c(bA + a)$

43. $bA - c$

44. $a[(b-c)A - b - cC]$

45. $\frac{1}{3}[\frac{A}{a} - \frac{B}{b} - \frac{C}{c}]$

46. $\frac{1}{b+c}[(a-b)A - (a+b)C]$

47. $\frac{bc}{a}(A - 1 - C)$

48. $(a + b)[\frac{A}{b} + \frac{1}{c} - \frac{C}{a}]$

49. $x = 2$

50. $x = 81$

51. $x = 1$

52. $x = 10$

53. $x = \pm 5$

54. $x = 0$

55.

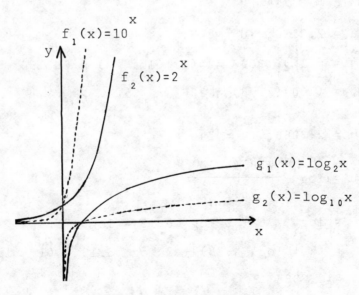

(a) at $(0,1)$ (b) at $(1,0)$

56. $(0,8)$ 57. $(0,1000)$ 58. $(\frac{1}{10},\infty)$ 59. $(\frac{1}{2},\infty)$

60. $(0,\infty)$ 61. $(2,\infty)$ 62. $(1,4)$ 63. $(-2,0) \cup (0,2)$

64. $(-\infty,-100) \cup (100,\infty)$ 65. $(0,1)$ 66. $(1,\infty)$

67. $(0,1)$

68. $\log_{10} u \cong 0.8480$, $u \cong 7.05$:

   $\log_{10} u = \frac{1}{3} \log_{10} 350 = \frac{1}{3}(2 + \log_{10} 3.5) \cong 0.8480$

69. $\log_{10} u \cong 0.6419$, $u \cong 4.38$:

   $\log_{10} u = \frac{1}{5} \log_{10} 1620 = \frac{1}{5}(3 + \log_{10} 1.62) \cong 0.6419$

70. $\log_{10} u \cong 2.3180$, $u \cong 208$:

   $\log_{10} u = \frac{2}{3} \log_{10} 3000 = \frac{2}{3}(3 + \log_{10} 3) \cong 2.3180$

   $u \cong (100)(2.08) = 208$

71. $\log_{10} u \cong 2.3866$, $u \cong 244$:

   $$\log_{10} u = \log_{10} \frac{(478)(6.19)^2}{75.2}$$

   $= \log_{10} 478 + 2 \log_{10} 6.19 - \log_{10} 75.2$

   $= (2 + \log_{10} 4.78) + 2 \log_{10} 6.19 - (1 + \log_{10} 7.52)$

   $\cong 2.3866$

   $u \cong 100(2.44) = 244$

72. $\log_{10} u \cong 1.0291, \quad u \cong 10.7$:

$$\log_{10} u = \log_{10} \frac{\sqrt{87} \ \sqrt[3]{70}}{\sqrt[5]{600}}$$

$$= \frac{1}{2} \log_{10} 87 + \frac{1}{3} \log_{10} 70 - \frac{1}{5} \log_{10} 600$$

$$= \frac{1}{2}(1 + \log_{10} 8.7) + \frac{1}{3}(1 + \log_{10} 7) - \frac{1}{5}(2 + \log_{10} 6)$$

$$\cong 1.0291$$

$$u \cong (10)(1.07) = 10.7$$

73. $x > 0$ 74. $x \neq 0$ 75. $x \neq a, b$ 76. $x > \max \{a, b\}$

77. $\log_B b = \dfrac{1}{\log_b B}$:   set $x = b$ in (5.7.7)

78. $\log_b x + \log_b (x-1) - \frac{1}{2} \log_b (x+1)$

79. $\log_b (x+1) + 3 \log_b (x-1) - \log_b x$

80. $\frac{1}{3} \log_b (x+1) - \frac{2}{3} \log_b x - \frac{2}{3} \log_b (x-1)$

81. $\frac{1}{2} \log_b (x+1) - \frac{1}{2} \log_b (x-1) - \log_b x$

82. $\frac{1}{2} \log_b x - \frac{5}{2} \log_b (x+1) - \frac{5}{2} \log_b (x-1)$

83. $5 \log_b x + \frac{5}{2} \log_b (x-1) - \frac{10}{3} \log_b (x+1)$ 84. $x > 1$

85. $\frac{1}{2} \log_b (1-x) + \frac{1}{2} \log_b (2-x) - \frac{1}{2} \log_b (3-x) - \frac{1}{2} \log_b (4-x)$

86. $2 \log_b (1-x) + \frac{1}{2} \log_b (2-x) - \frac{1}{2} \log_b (3-x) - 2 \log_b (4-x)$

87. $\frac{1}{3} \log_b (1-x) + \frac{1}{3} \log_b (2-x) - 2 \log_b (3-x) - 2 \log_b (4-x)$

88. $5 \log_b (1-x) + \frac{5}{2} \log_b (2-x) - \frac{5}{3} \log_b (3-x) - \frac{5}{4} \log_b (4-x)$

89. $x < 1$ 90. $x = 5$ 91. $x = \frac{8}{7}$ 92. $x = 15$

93. $x = \frac{1}{3}$ 94. $x = 100, x = 1$ 95. $x = \frac{1}{9}$

96. $x = 625$ 97. $x = 1$ 98. $x(x^2 - 1)$ 99. $\dfrac{x}{x^2 - 1}$

100. $\dfrac{x(x + 1)^2}{(x - 1)^3}$ 101. $\dfrac{x^3}{\sqrt{x^2 - 1}}$ 102. $\dfrac{\sqrt{x}(x+1)^3}{(x-1)^2}$ 103. $\dfrac{(x- 1)^2}{x^2\sqrt{x+1}}$

104. (a) $g^{-1}(x) = 2^x + 1$ 105. (a) $f^{-1}(x) = 1 + \log_2 x$

(b)   (b)

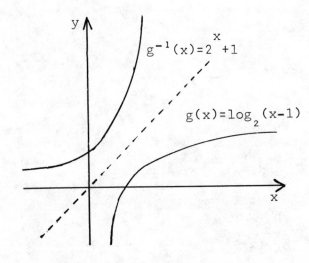

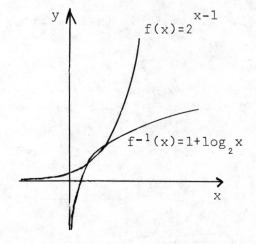

106. (a) below   (b) $g = \frac{1}{2}f$

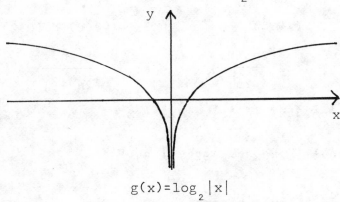

$g(x)=\log_2|x|$

107. (a) →

(b) $g^{-1}(x) = -2^x$

(c) below

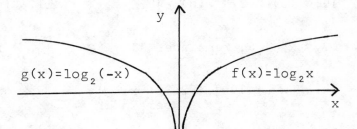

$g(x)=\log_2(-x)$ $f(x)=\log_2 x$

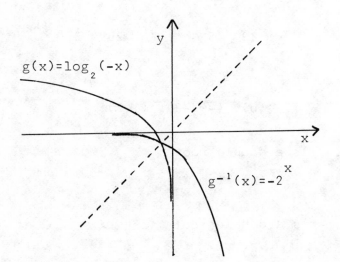

$g(x)=\log_2(-x)$

$g^{-1}(x)=-2^x$

SECTION 5.8

1. $(0,2)$ 2. $(-\infty, \frac{3}{2})$ 3. $(-2,0) \cup (0,2)$

4. $(-\infty, -\frac{5}{3}) \cup (0, \frac{5}{3})$ 5. $(-\infty, \frac{2n+1}{2n})$ 6. $(0, \frac{2n}{2n-1})$

7. $1 + 7x + 21x^2 + 35x^3 + 35x^4 + 21x^5 + 7x^6 + x^7$

8. $1 - 12x + 60x^2 - 160x^3 + 240x^4 - 192x^5 + 64x^6$

9. $32 - \frac{80}{3}x + \frac{80}{9}x^2 - \frac{40}{27}x^3 + \frac{10}{81}x^4 - \frac{1}{243}x^5$

10. (a) 252   (b) -462   11. (a) -455   (b) 1140

12. $x^2 - 5$, remainder 11   13. $5x^3 + 6x^2 + 11x + 33$, remainder 96

14. $4x^4 + 10x^3 + 2x^2 + x + \frac{1}{2}$, remainder $\frac{33}{4}$ 15. $9x^5 - 21x^3 + 3x^2 + 6x$

16. $P(-2) = 83$, $P(2) = -5$ 17. $P(3) = 1114$, $P(-3) = -404$

18. $P(\frac{3}{5}) = 0$, $P(\frac{5}{3}) = 0$ 19. 5   20. 3

21. -3, 1, 2 are simple roots

    (a) $(-3,1)$, $(2,\infty)$ (b) $(-\infty,-3)$, $(1,2)$

22. $-\frac{3}{2}$ is a simple root, 1 is a double root

    (a) $(-\frac{3}{2},1)$, $(1,\infty)$ (b) $(-\infty,-\frac{3}{2})$

23. -3 is a simple root, $\frac{1}{2}$ is a double root

    (a) $(-3,\frac{1}{2})$, $(\frac{1}{2},\infty)$ (b) $(-\infty,-3)$

24. -1 is a simple root, 2 is a triple root

    (a) $(-\infty,-1)$, $(2,\infty)$ (b) $(-1,2)$

25. -2 and $-\frac{1}{2}$ are both double roots

    (a) $(-\infty,-2)$, $(-2,-\frac{1}{2})$, $(-\frac{1}{2},\infty)$ (b) ϕ

26. -1 and 2 are simple roots, 3 is a double root

    (a) $(-\infty,-1)$, $(2,3)$, $(3,\infty)$ (b) $(-1,2)$

27. $\frac{1}{2}$ and 1 are simple roots

    (a) $(-\infty,\frac{1}{2})$, $(1,\infty)$ (b) $(\frac{1}{2},1)$

28. $-\frac{2}{3}$ is a simple root, 1 is a root of multiplicity 4

    (a) $(-\frac{2}{3},1)$, $(1,\infty)$ (b) $(-\infty,-\frac{2}{3})$

29. $-\frac{5}{2}$, $-\frac{2}{5}$, 1, and 2 are simple roots

    (a) $(-\infty,-\frac{5}{2})$, $(-\frac{2}{5},1)$, $(2,\infty)$ (b) $(-\frac{5}{2},-\frac{2}{5})$, $(1,2)$

30. $\frac{1}{3}$ is a simple root

    (a) $(\frac{1}{3},\infty)$ (b) $(-\infty,\frac{1}{3})$

31. (a) $4800: 8000(1.60) = 12,800.00$

    (b) about $4695: 8000(1.08)^6 \cong 8000(1.5869) = 12,695.20$

    (c) about $7790: 8000(1.12)^6 \cong 8000(1.9738) = 15,790.40$

    (d) about $4808: 8000(1.04)^{12} \cong 8000(1.6010) = 12,808.00$

    (e) about $6367: 8000(1.05)^{12} \cong 8000(1.7959) = 14,367.20$

    (f) about $4867: 8000(1.02)^{24} \cong 8000(1.6084) = 12,867.20$

    (g) about $8306: 8000(1.03)^{24} \cong 8000(2.0382) = 16,305.60$

32. (a) about \$13,401: $10,500(1.05)^5 \cong 10,500(1.2763) = 13,401.15$

  (b) about \$15,428: $10,500(1.08)^5 \cong 10,500(1.4693) = 15,427.65$

  (c) about \$18,504: $10,500(1.12)^5 \cong 10,500(1.7623) = 18,504.15$

33. (a) about \$7835: $10,000(1.05)^{-5} \cong 10,500(0.7835) = 7835$

  (b) about \$7410: $10,000(1.03)^{-10} \cong 10,000(0.7410) = 7410$

  (c) about \$6730: $10,000(1.02)^{-20} \cong 10,000(0.6730) = 6730$

34. about \$32,578: $20,000(1.05)^{10} \cong 20,000(1.6289) = 32,578$

35. $r = k^{1/n} - 1$:

$$kP = P(1 + r)^n$$
$$k = (1 + r)^n$$
$$k^{1/n} = 1 + r$$
$$r = k^{1/n} - 1$$

36. (a) $1/r$ years:

$$2P = P(1 + nr)$$
$$2 = (1 + nr)$$
$$1 = nr$$
$$n = 1/r$$

(b) $\dfrac{1}{\log_2(1 + r)}$ years:

$$2P = P(1 + r)^n$$
$$2 = (1 + r)^n$$
$$1 = n \log_2(1 + r)$$
$$n = \frac{1}{\log_2(1 + r)}$$

(c) $\dfrac{1}{q \log_2(1 + \frac{r}{q})}$ years:

$$2P = P(1 + \frac{r}{q})^{nq}$$
$$2 = (1 + \frac{r}{q})^{nq}$$
$$1 = nq \log_2(1 + \frac{r}{q})$$
$$n = \frac{1}{q \log_2(1 + \frac{r}{q})}$$

37. $f^{-1}(x) = \frac{1}{2}(b^x - 3)$

38. $f^{-1}(x) = \frac{1}{2}(\log_b x - 3)$

39. $f^{-1}(x) = -\dfrac{b^x + 1}{b^x - 1}$

40. $f^{-1}(x) = -\dfrac{\log_b x + 1}{\log_b x - 1}$.

41. $(-\infty, 0)$

42. $(-\infty, -1) \cup (0, 1)$

43. (b^2, b^5)

44. $(\log_b 2, \log_b 5)$

45. $(\frac{1}{3}, \infty)$

46. $(0, 1) \cup (1, \infty)$

47. $(-2, 2)$

48. $(-2, -1) \cup (1, 2)$

49. $(-\infty, -\sqrt{2}) \cup (\sqrt{2}, \infty)$

50. $(-2, -\sqrt{2}) \cup (\sqrt{2}, 2)$

51. $k = 0$ or $k = 1$:

If $k = 0$, the polynomial is constant, say $P(x) = c$; then

$$\frac{P(x_1) + P(x_2)}{2} = \frac{c + c}{2} = c = P\left(\frac{x_1 + x_2}{2}\right).$$

If $k = 1$, the polynomial is linear, say $P(x) = ax + b$; then

$$\frac{P(x_1) + P(x_2)}{2} = \frac{(ax_1 + b)(ax_2 + b)}{2}$$

$$= \frac{a(x_1 + x_2) + 2b}{2}$$

$$= a\left(\frac{x_1 + x_2}{2}\right) + b = P\left(\frac{x_1 + x_2}{2}\right).$$

If $k > 1$, then $P(x) = x^k$ fails to satisfy the condition:

$$\frac{P(0) + P(1)}{2} = \frac{1}{2}, \qquad P(\tfrac{1}{2}) = (\tfrac{1}{2})^k \neq \frac{1}{2} \quad \text{for } k > 1.$$

52. It's easy to see that

$$P(-2) < 0, \quad P(0) > 0, \quad P(1) < 0, \quad P(2) > 0.$$

   Thus there is a root in $(-2,0)$, a root in $(0,1)$, and a root in $(1,2)$.

53. The polynomial $Q(x) = P(x) - C$ satisfies

$$Q(a) = P(a) - C < 0, \quad Q(b) = P(b) - C > 0.$$

   Thus by (5.8.1) there is a number c between a and b for which $Q(c) = 0$. This means that

$$P(c) - C = 0 \quad \text{and} \quad P(c) = C.$$

54. If $a_0 > 0$, then, n being odd, $a_0 x^n > 0$ for $x > 0$ and $a_0 x^n < 0$ for $x < 0$. Thus $P(x) > 0$ for all positive x sufficiently far from the origin and $P(x) < 0$ for all negative x sufficiently far from the origin. By (5.8.1) the equation $P(x) = 0$ must have a root somewhere in between. The case $a_0 < 0$ is similar.

55. (a) $a_0 > 0$ (b) $a_0 < 0$

   (c) $a_0 > 0$ and n is even, or, $a_0 < 0$ and n is odd

   (d) $a_0 < 0$ and n is even, or, $a_0 > 0$ and n is odd

   (e) $a_0 > 0$ and n is even   (f) $a_0 < 0$ and n is even

   (g) $a_0 > 0$ and n is odd   (h) $a_0 < 0$ and n is odd

56. 2^n (the total number of subsets that can be extracted from a set of n elements)

57. $R(t) = R_0 2^{-t/1600}$

58. (a) about 3200 years   (b) about 4800 years

   (c) about $\dfrac{1600}{\log_{10} 2}$ years   (about 5316 years)

59. (a) $T = \dfrac{20}{\log_2 R_0 - \log_2 R_1}$ years:

$$R_1 = R_0 2^{-20/T}$$

$$\frac{R_1}{R_0} = 2^{-20/T}$$

$$\log_2 R_1 - \log_2 R_0 = -\frac{20}{T}$$

$$T = \frac{20}{\log_2 R_0 - \log_2 R_1} \text{ years.}$$

(b) $T = \dfrac{n}{\log_2 R_0 - \log_2 R_1}$ years

60. (a) $R_0 \left(\dfrac{R_1}{R_0}\right)^2$:

Take 5 years ago as time 0. Today $t = 5$.

$$R_1 = R(5) = R_0 2^{-5/T}$$

$$\frac{R_1}{R_0} = 2^{-5/T} .$$

Five years from now, t will equal 10 and the radioactivity will be

$$R_0 2^{-10/T} = R_0 (2^{-5/T})^2 = R_0 \left(\frac{R_1}{R_0}\right)^2 .$$

(b) $R_0 \left(\dfrac{R_1}{R_0}\right)^3$ (c) $R_0 \left(\dfrac{R_1}{R_0}\right)^{k+1}$ (d) $R_0 \left(\dfrac{R_1}{R_0}\right)^{(n/5)+1}$

SECTION 6.1

1. opposite side: $2 \sin 50° \cong 1.53$

    adjacent side: $2 \cos 50° \cong 1.29$

2. opposite side: $2.5 \tan 34° \cong 1.69$

    hypotenuse: $\dfrac{2.5}{\cos 34°} \cong 3.02$

3. adjacent side: $\dfrac{10}{\tan 60°} \cong 5.77$

    hypotenuse: $\dfrac{10}{\sin 60°} \cong 11.55$

4. adjacent side: $\dfrac{2.6}{\tan 10°} \cong 14.75$

    hypotenuse: $\dfrac{2.6}{\sin 10°} \cong 14.98$

5. angle: $\sin A = \dfrac{1.44}{12} = 0.1200, \quad A \cong 7°$

    other leg: $12 \cos 7° \cong 11.91$

6. angle: $\sin A = \dfrac{7}{10} = 0.7000, \quad A \cong 44°$

    other leg: $10 \cos 44° \cong 7.19$

7. adjacent side: $\dfrac{4}{\tan 19°} \cong 11.62$

    hypotenuse: $\dfrac{4}{\sin 19°} \cong 12.29$

8. angle: $\tan A = \dfrac{3.2}{6.5} \cong 0.4923, \quad A \cong 26°$

hypotenuse: $\dfrac{3.2}{\sin 26°} \cong 7.30$

9. $\sin 45° = \dfrac{1}{\sqrt{2}} = \dfrac{1}{2}\sqrt{2}, \quad \cos 45° = \dfrac{1}{\sqrt{2}} = \dfrac{1}{2}\sqrt{2}, \quad \tan 45° = \dfrac{1}{1} = 1$

10. about 23° and 67°

11. $\tan A = \dfrac{\sin A}{\cos A}$

12. $\sin(90°-A) = \cos A$

13. $\cos(90°-A) = \sin A$

14. $\tan(90°-A) = \dfrac{1}{\tan A}$

15. 1

16. By similar triangles

$$\frac{a}{a'} = \frac{c}{c'}, \qquad \frac{b}{b'} = \frac{c}{c'}, \qquad \frac{a}{a'} = \frac{b}{b'}.$$

Thus

$$\frac{a}{c} = \frac{a'}{c'}, \qquad \frac{b}{c} = \frac{b'}{c'}, \qquad \frac{a}{b} = \frac{a'}{b'}.$$

The first equation shows that sin A is the same from both triangles; the second equation shows that cos A is the same from both triangles; the third equation shows that tan A is the same from both triangles.

SECTION 6.2

1. $N = 2 \cos 10° \cong 1.97$ (about 1.97 miles north)

$E = 2 \sin 10° \cong 0.35$ (about 0.35 miles east)

2. S = 5 cos 20° $\cong$ 4.70   (about 4.70 miles south)

    W = 5 sin 20° $\cong$ 1.71   (about 1.71 miles west)

3. distance from X: $\dfrac{3.41}{\tan 43°}$ $\cong$ 3.66   (about 3.66 miles)

    distance from Y: $\dfrac{3.41}{\sin 43°}$ $\cong$ 5   (about 5 miles)

4. 6(4 sin 74°) $\cong$ 23.07

5. 2(4 sin 25°) $\cong$ 3.38

6. 2 tan 35° $\cong$ 1.40   (about 1.4 miles; i.e. about 7392 feet)

7. 50 tan 33° $\cong$ 32.47   (about 32.47 feet)

8. $\dfrac{20}{\tan 50°}$ $\cong$ 228.57   (about 228.57 feet)

9. $\dfrac{80}{\cos 64°}$ $\cong$ 182.48   (about 182.48 feet)

10. 100 tan 88° $\cong$ 2864   (about 2864 feet)

11. tan A = $\dfrac{120}{40}$ = 3,

    A $\cong$ 72°

    B = 180° − 2A $\cong$ 36°

    C = 180° − α $\cong$ 144°

    appox 36° and 144°

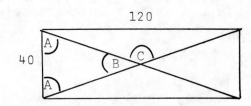

12. $\dfrac{7}{\tan 20°} \cong 19.23$ (about 19.23 feet away)

13. (a) $400 \sin 70° \cong 375.88$ (about 375.88 feet)

    (b) $200\sqrt{3}$ feet

14. $\frac{2}{3}h = 20 \cos 15° \cong 19.32,$ $h \cong 28.98$ (about 28.98 feet)

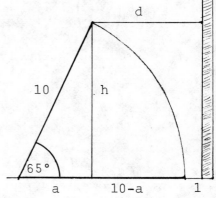

15. $a = 10 \cos 65° \cong 4.226$

    $d = (10-a) + 1 \cong 6.774$

    $h = 10 \sin 65° \cong 9.063$

    moved about 6.77 feet
    closer to the wall;
    about 9.06 feet high

16. $\tan A = \dfrac{h}{x},$ $\tan B = \dfrac{h}{s-x}$

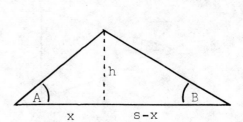

    $x \tan A = h,$ $(s-x) \tan B = h$

        $x \tan A = (s-x) \tan B$

    $x(\tan A + \tan B) = s \tan B$

$$x = \frac{s \tan B}{\tan A + \tan B}.$$

The relation $h = x \tan A$ gives

$$h = \frac{s \tan A \tan B}{\tan A + \tan B}.$$

17. $p_n = 2n \sin\left(\dfrac{360°}{2n}\right)$

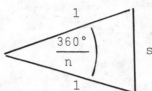 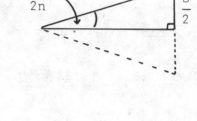

$\dfrac{s}{2} = \sin\left(\dfrac{360°}{2n}\right)$

$p_n = ns = 2n\dfrac{s}{2} = 2n \sin\left(\dfrac{360°}{2n}\right)$

18. $\pi \overset{\sim}{=} p_{36}/2 = 36 \sin 5° \overset{\sim}{=} 36(0.0872) = 3.1392 \overset{\sim}{=} 3.14$

19. $P_n = 2n \tan\left(\dfrac{360°}{2n}\right)$

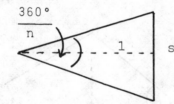 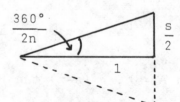

$\dfrac{s}{2} = \tan\left(\dfrac{360°}{2n}\right)$

$P_n = ns = 2n\dfrac{s}{2} = 2n \tan\left(\dfrac{360°}{2n}\right)$

20. $\pi \overset{\sim}{=} P_{36}/2 = 36 \tan 5° \overset{\sim}{=} 36(0.0875) \overset{\sim}{=} 3.15$

SECTION 6.3

1. $\frac{1}{2}\sqrt{3}$ 2. $-\frac{1}{2}$ 3. $-\sqrt{3}$ 4. -1 5. 0

6. 0 7. 2 8. $\frac{2}{3}\sqrt{3}$ 9. $\frac{1}{3}\sqrt{3}$ 10. -1

11. -1 12. 0 13. 1 14. 1 15. 0

16. $-\frac{1}{2}\sqrt{3}$ 17. $-\frac{1}{2}$ 18. $\frac{1}{3}\sqrt{3}$ 19. $-\frac{1}{2}\sqrt{3}$ 20. $\frac{1}{2}$

21. $-\sqrt{3}$ 22. $\sqrt{2}$ 23. $-\sqrt{2}$ 24. -1 25. 0

26. 0 27. $-\frac{1}{2}$ 28. -2 29. 1 30. 0

31. 0.9063 32. -0.4226 33. -2.145

34. -2.366 35. -0.3420 36. 0.9397

37. -0.3640 38. 1.064 39. 0.1736

40. 0.9848 41. 0.1763 42. 1.015

43. $\cot 15° = \tan 75° \stackrel{\sim}{=} 3.732$ 44. -0.2679

45. -0.4663 46. 3.864 47. -1.035

48. 1.103 49. -5.671 50. -5.759

51. 1.192

52. Sin 1° is not exactly 0.0175. This is only a four-place decimal approximation. (Rounded off to five decimal places, sin 1° $\stackrel{\sim}{=}$ 0.01745.) Division by the decimal magnifies the error.

53. (a) 90°, 270°   (b) all odd multiples of ±90°

(c) 0°, 180°, 360°   (d) all even multiples of ±90°

54. (a) I, IV   (b) II, III   (c) I, II

(d) III, IV   (e) I, III   (f) II, IV

55. (a) $\cos A = \frac{4}{5}$, $\tan A = \frac{3}{4}$ (b) $\cos A = -\frac{4}{5}$, $\tan A = -\frac{3}{4}$

56. (a) $\sin A = \frac{4}{5}$, $\tan A = -\frac{4}{3}$ (b) $\sin A = -\frac{4}{5}$, $\tan A = \frac{4}{3}$

57. (a) $\cos A = -\frac{4}{5}$, $\sin A = \frac{3}{5}$ (b) $\cos A = \frac{4}{5}$, $\sin A = -\frac{3}{5}$

58. $- \tan A$ 59. $\sec A$ 60. $- \csc A$

61. $\tan A$ 62. $\cot A$ 63. $- \sec A$

64. $- \tan A$ 65. $- \sec A$ 66. $\csc A$

67. $\sec^2 A$ 68. $\csc^2 A$ 69. $\tan^2 A$

70. 0°, 360°   71. 180°   72. 90°

73. 270°   74. 0°, 180°, 360°   75. 45°, 225°

76. 135°, 315°   77. 60°, 300°   78. 30°, 150°

79. 210°, 330°   80. 120°, 240°   81. 240°, 300°

82. 60°, 300°   83. $0° < A < 90°$

SECTION 6.4

1. $C = 60°$, $\quad a = \dfrac{6 \sin 40°}{\sin 60°} = 6 \sin 40° \sec 30° \cong 4.45$

    $b = \dfrac{6 \sin 80°}{\sin 60°} = 6 \sin 80° \sec 30° \cong 6.82$

2. $B = 108°$, $\quad a = \dfrac{24 \sin 16°}{\sin 108°} = 24 \sin 16° \sec 18° \cong 6.95$

    $c = \dfrac{24 \sin 56°}{\sin 108°} = 24 \sin 56° \sec 18° \cong 20.91$

3. $49 = 64 + 81 - 2(8)(9) \cos A$, $\quad \cos A \cong 0.6667$, $\quad A \cong 48°$

    $64 = 49 + 81 - 2(7)(9) \cos B$, $\quad \cos B \cong 0.5238$, $\quad B \cong 58°$

    $C \cong 180° - 48° - 58° = 74°$

4. $36 = 121 + 225 - 2(11)(15) \cos A$, $\quad \cos A \cong 0.9394$, $\quad A \cong 20°$

    $121 = 36 + 225 - 2(6)(15) \cos B$, $\quad \cos B \cong 0.7778$, $\quad B \cong 39°$

    $C \cong 180° - 20° - 39° = 121°$

5. $A = 150°$, $\quad b = \dfrac{100 \sin 10°}{\sin 150°} = \dfrac{100 \sin 10°}{1/2} \cong 34.72$

    $c = \dfrac{100 \sin 20°}{\sin 150°} = \dfrac{100 \sin 20°}{1/2} \cong 68.40$

6. $1.21 = 4 + 9 - 2(2)(3) \cos A$, $\quad \cos A \cong 0.9825$, $\quad A \cong 11°$

    $4 = 1.21 + 9 - 2(1.1)(3) \cos B$, $\cos B \cong 0.9409$, $\quad B \cong 20°$

    $C \cong 180° - 11° - 20° = 149°$

7. $A = 70°$, $B = 70°$ (isoceles triangle)

$$c = \frac{10 \sin 40°}{\sin 70°} = 10 \sin 40° \sec 20° \cong 6.84$$

8. $B = 90°$, $a = 4 \cos 30° \cong 3.4640$, $c = 4 \sin 30° = 2$

9. $b^2 = 4 + 16 - 2(2)(4) \cos 12° \cong 4.3504$, $b \cong 2.086$

 (square root table)

$$\sin A = \frac{4 \sin 12°}{2.086} \cong 0.3987, \quad A \cong 156.5°$$

$C \cong 180° - 12° - 156.5° = 11.5°$

10. $A = 100°$, $b = \dfrac{10 \sin 50°}{\sin 100°} = 10 \sin 50° \sec 10° \cong 7.77$

$$c = \frac{10 \sin 30°}{\sin 100°} = 10 \sin 30° \sec 10° \cong 5.08$$

11. $1.44 = 1.69 + 4 - 2(1.3)(2) \cos A$, $\cos A \cong 0.8173$, $A \cong 35°$

 $1.69 = 1.44 + 4 - 2(1.2)(2) \cos B$, $\cos B \cong 0.7813$, $B \cong 39°$

 $C \cong 180° - 35° - 39° = 106°$

12. $a^2 = 38.44 + 49 - 2(6.2)(7) \cos 60° \cong 44.04$, $a \cong 6.633$

 (square root table)

$$\sin B = \frac{6.2 \sin 60°}{6.633} \cong 0.8095, \quad B \cong 54°$$

$C \cong 180° - 60° - 54° = 66°$

13. $C = 40°$, $a = \dfrac{5 \sin 79°}{\sin 40°} = 5 \sin 79° \sec 50° \cong 7.64$

$$b = \frac{5 \sin 61°}{\sin 40°} = 5 \sin 61° \sec 50° \cong 6.80$$

14. $400 = 100 + 225 - 2(10)(15) \cos A$, $\cos A = -0.2500$, $A \cong 104°$

$100 = 400 + 225 - 2(20)(15) \cos B$, $\cos B = 0.8750$, $B \cong 29°$

$C \cong 180° - 104° - 29° = 47°$

15. $d^2 = 25 + 4900 - 2(5)(70) \cos 45° \cong 4430.03$, $d \cong 66.56$

(about 66.56 miles)

16. $b = \dfrac{10 \sin 135°}{\sin 25°} = 10 \sin 45° \sec 65° \cong 16.73$

distance from A about 16.73 miles

$a = \dfrac{10 \sin 20°}{\sin 25°} = 10 \sin 20° \sec 65° \cong 8.09$

distance from B about 8.09 miles

17. about 2.78

18. $d^2 = 64 + 144 - 2(8)(12) \cos 70°$

$\cong 142.34$

$d \cong 11.92$ about 11.92 miles

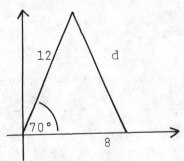

19. It follows directly from the law of sines. For instance

$\dfrac{\sin A}{a} = \dfrac{\sin B}{b} \rightarrow b \sin A = a \sin B \rightarrow bc \sin A = ac \sin B.$

20. (a)   area $= \frac{1}{2}ab \sin C$

(b)   Set $a = 2$, $b = 3$, $c = 4$. The law of cosines gives

$\cos C = -\frac{1}{4}$ and thus

$\sin C = \sqrt{1 - \dfrac{1}{16}} = \sqrt{\dfrac{15}{16}} = \frac{1}{4}\sqrt{15}.$

Therefore

$$\text{area} = \tfrac{1}{2}ab \sin C = \tfrac{1}{2}(2)(3)\tfrac{1}{4}\sqrt{15} = \tfrac{1}{4}\sqrt{15}.$$

(c) $\frac{15}{4}\sqrt{7}$

21. $\cos C = \dfrac{x}{a}$, $\sin C = \dfrac{h}{a}$

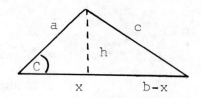

$a \cos C = x$, $a \sin C = h$

By the Pythagorean theorem

$$c^2 = (b - x)^2 + h^2.$$

Substituting $a \cos C$ for x and $a \sin C$ for h, we have

$$c^2 = (b - a \cos C)^2 + (a \sin C)^2$$

$$= b^2 - 2ab \cos C + a^2 \cos^2 C + a^2 \sin^2 C$$

$$= b^2 - 2ab \cos C + a^2(\cos^2 C + \sin^2 C)$$

$$= b^2 - 2ab \cos C + a^2$$

$$= a^2 + b^2 - 2ab \cos C.$$

SECTION 6.5

1. (a) $\frac{3}{2}\pi$ radians   (b) $\frac{4}{3}\pi$ radians   (c) $-\frac{5}{3}\pi$ radians

    (d) $-\frac{1}{12}\pi$ radians   (e) $\frac{5}{12}\pi$ radians   (f) $-\frac{11}{12}\pi$ radians

2. (a) $540°$ (b) $270°$ (c) $-180°$

    (d) $-67.5°$ (e) $292.5°$ (f) $-12°$

3. 4 revolutions per second

4. (a) $2\pi n$ radians per second   (b) $360n$ degrees per second

5. (a) the area increases by a factor of k

    (b) the area increases by a factor of k^2

6. $\frac{1}{2}(r + h)^2\theta - \frac{1}{2}r^2\theta = \frac{1}{2}(2r + h)h\theta$

7. $\theta = \frac{5}{8}$ radians, $L = \frac{15}{8}$

8. the middle wheel rotates clockwise at the rate of 2θ radians per second; the smallest wheel rotates at the rate of 4θ radians per second

9. $r = 4$, $\theta = \frac{3}{4}\pi$

    length of subtended arc = $r\theta = 4(\frac{3}{4}\pi) = 3\pi$

    area = $\frac{1}{2}r^2\theta = \frac{1}{2}(16)(\frac{3}{4}\pi) = 6\pi$

10. $r = 2$, $\theta = \frac{1}{6}\pi$

    length of subtended arc = $r\theta = 2(\frac{1}{6}\pi) = \frac{1}{3}\pi$

    area = $\frac{1}{2}r^2\theta = \frac{1}{2}(4)(\frac{1}{6}\pi) = \frac{1}{3}\pi$

11. $r = 5$

    length of arc = $r\theta$

    $\qquad\qquad 3\pi = 5\theta$

    $\qquad\qquad\quad \theta = \frac{3}{5}\pi$ the central angle measures $\frac{3}{5}\pi$ radians

    area of sector = $\frac{1}{2}r^2\theta = \frac{1}{2}(25)(\frac{3}{5}\pi) = \frac{15}{2}\pi$

12. $\frac{1}{2}r_1^2\theta = \frac{1}{2}r_2^2(3\theta)$

    $r_1^2\theta = 3r_2^2\theta$

    $r_1 = \sqrt{3}\, r_2$

13. (a) θ ft per second   (b) $r\theta$ ft per second

14. the larger wheel turns counterclockwise at the rate of $\frac{1}{3}\theta$ radians per second; the speed of the belt is 3θ inches per second

SECTION 6.6

1. $\frac{1}{4}\pi + 2n\pi$, n an integer ≥ 0 2. $\frac{11}{6}\pi + 2n\pi$, n an integer ≥ 0

3. $\pi + 2n\pi$, n an integer ≥ 0 4. $\frac{19}{12}\pi + 2n\pi$, n an integer ≥ 0

5. $-\frac{7}{4}\pi - 2n\pi$, n an integer ≥ 0 6. $-\frac{1}{6}\pi - 2n\pi$, n an integer ≥ 0

7. $-\pi - 2n\pi$, n an integer ≥ 0 8. $-\frac{5}{12}\pi - 2n\pi$, n an integer ≥ 0

9. -1 10. 0   11. -1 12. 0

13. -1 14. 0   15. 0   16. 1

17. $\frac{1}{2}$ 18. $-\frac{1}{2}\sqrt{3}$ 19. $\frac{1}{2}\sqrt{3}$ 20. $\frac{1}{2}$

21. $\frac{1}{2}\sqrt{2}$ 22. $-\frac{1}{2}\sqrt{2}$ 23. $\frac{1}{2}$ 24. $-\frac{1}{2}\sqrt{3}$

25. 0   26. -1 27. $\frac{1}{2}\sqrt{3}$ 28. $-\frac{1}{2}$

29. 0   30. -1 31. $\frac{1}{2}\sqrt{3}$ 32. $-\frac{1}{2}$

33. -1 34. 0   35. $\frac{1}{2}\sqrt{2}$ 36. $\frac{1}{2}\sqrt{2}$

37. $\frac{1}{2}\pi, \frac{3}{2}\pi$ 38. 0, π, 2π 39. 0, 2π 40. $\frac{1}{2}\pi$

41. $\frac{1}{3}\pi$, $\frac{5}{3}\pi$ 42. $\frac{1}{6}\pi$, $\frac{5}{6}\pi$ 43. π 44. $\frac{3}{2}\pi$

45. $\frac{1}{4}\pi$, $\frac{7}{4}\pi$ 46. $\frac{5}{4}\pi$, $\frac{7}{4}\pi$ 47. $\frac{1}{6}\pi$, $\frac{11}{6}\pi$ 48. $\frac{1}{3}\pi$, $\frac{2}{3}\pi$

49. $\cos^2 t + \sin^2 t = 1$ 50. $\cos^2 t + \sin^2 t = 1$

$\cos^2 t + 4\cos^2 t = 1$ $\cos^2 t + \frac{16}{9}\cos^2 t = 1$

           $5\cos^2 t = 1$ $\frac{25}{9}\cos^2 t = 1$

              $\cos t = \pm\frac{1}{5}\sqrt{5}$ $\cos t = \pm\frac{3}{5}$

51. $\cos^2 t + \sin^2 t = 1$ 52. (a) $\frac{4}{5}$ (b) $-\frac{4}{5}$

$\cos^2 t + \frac{4}{49}\cos^2 t = 1$

         $\frac{53}{49}\cos^2 t = 1$

            $\cos t = \pm\frac{7}{53}\sqrt{53}$

53. (a) $-\frac{12}{13}$ (b) $\frac{12}{13}$ 54. $\frac{1}{4}\pi$, $\frac{5}{4}\pi$ 55. $\frac{3}{4}\pi$, $\frac{7}{4}\pi$

56. $\frac{5}{6}\pi$, $\frac{11}{6}\pi$ 57. $\frac{1}{2}r^2(t - \sin t)$

58. (a) $\cos (t + \frac{1}{2}\pi) = -\sin t$ since, moving clockwise, the first
coordinate of each of the four points is the negative of
the second coordinate of the previous point;
$\sin (t + \frac{1}{2}\pi) = \cos t$ since, moving counterclockwise, the
second coordinate of each of the four points is the first
coordinate of the previous point.

(b) $\cos (\frac{1}{2}\pi - t) = \cos (-t + \frac{1}{2}\pi) = -\sin (-t) = \sin t$

           by (6.6.8)⎯⎯⎯↑

     $\sin (\frac{1}{2}\pi - t) = \sin (-t + \frac{1}{2}\pi) = \cos (-t) = \cos t$

           by (6.6.8)⎯⎯⎯↑

SECTION 6.7

1. amplitude 1, period $\frac{8}{3}\pi$

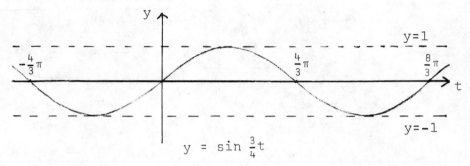

$$y = \sin \frac{3}{4}t$$

2. amplitude 1, period $\frac{8}{3}\pi$

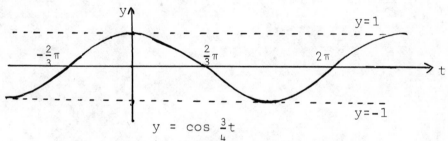

$$y = \cos \frac{3}{4}t$$

3. amplitude $\frac{3}{4}$, period 2π

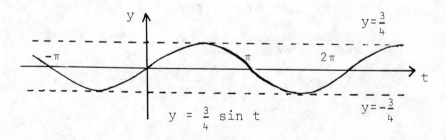

$$y = \frac{3}{4}\sin t$$

4. amplitude $\frac{3}{4}$, period 2π

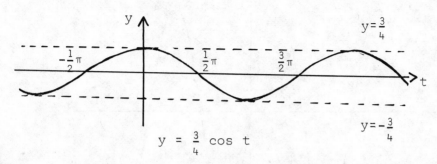

$$y = \frac{3}{4} \cos t$$

5. amplitude 1, period π

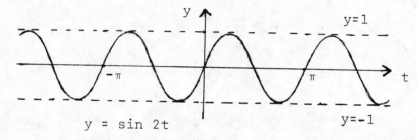

$$y = \sin 2t$$

6. amplitude 1, period π

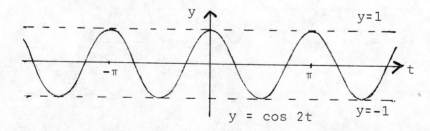

$$y = \cos 2t$$

7. amplitude $\frac{1}{2}$, period π

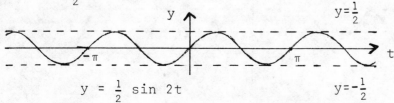

$$y = \frac{1}{2} \sin 2t$$

8. amplitude 3, period π

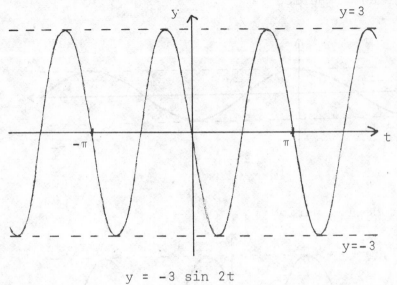

$$y = -3 \sin 2t$$

9. amplitude 1, period 2

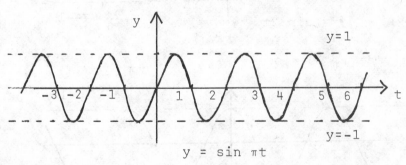

$$y = \sin \pi t$$

10. amplitude $\frac{2}{3}$, period 2

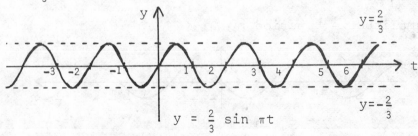

$$y = \frac{2}{3} \sin \pi t$$

11. amplitude $\frac{2}{3}$, period 2

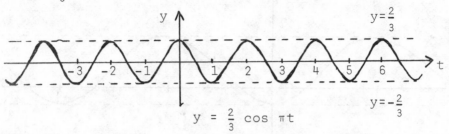

$$y = \frac{2}{3} \cos \pi t$$

12. amplitude $\frac{1}{3}$, period 4

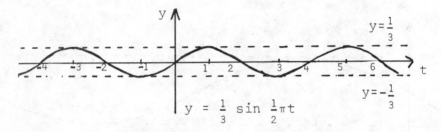

$$y = \frac{1}{3} \sin \frac{1}{2}\pi t$$

13. the sine curve raised one unit

14. the cosine curve raised two units

15.

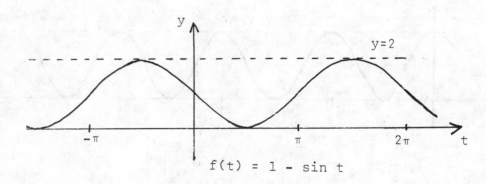

$$f(t) = 1 - \sin t$$

16.

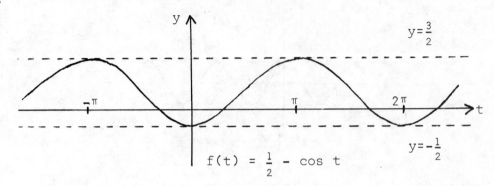

$$f(t) = \frac{1}{2} - \cos t$$

17.

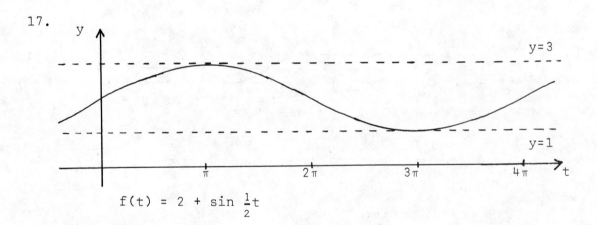

$$f(t) = 2 + \sin \frac{1}{2}t$$

18.

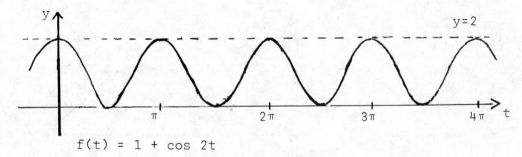

$$f(t) = 1 + \cos 2t$$

19. amplitude $\frac{5}{3}$, period 2π, y-intercept 0

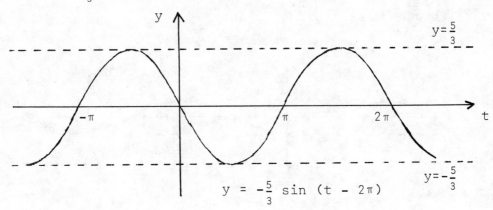

$$y = -\frac{5}{3} \sin (t - 2\pi)$$

20. $y = \frac{1}{5} \sin (\pi - 2t) = -\frac{1}{5} \sin (2t - \pi) = \frac{1}{5} \sin 2t$

amplitude $\frac{1}{5}$, period π, y-intercept 0

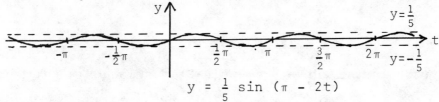

$$y = \frac{1}{5} \sin (\pi - 2t)$$

21. $y = -\frac{1}{3} \sin (\frac{1}{2}\pi - t) = \frac{1}{3} \sin (t - \frac{1}{2}\pi) = \frac{1}{3} \sin (t + \frac{3}{2}\pi)$

amplitude $\frac{1}{3}$, period 2π, y-intercept $-\frac{1}{3}$

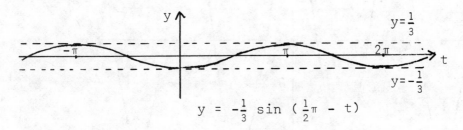

$$y = -\frac{1}{3} \sin (\frac{1}{2}\pi - t)$$

22. $y = \frac{1}{2} \cos(\pi - t) = \frac{1}{2} \cos(t - \pi) = \frac{1}{2} \cos(t + \pi) = -\frac{1}{2} \cos t$

amplitude $\frac{1}{2}$, period 2π, y-intercept $-\frac{1}{2}$

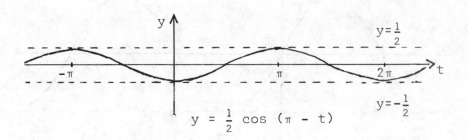

$$y = \frac{1}{2} \cos (\pi - t)$$

23. amplitude 3, period π, y-intercept 3

Since

$$3 \sin (2t + \frac{1}{2}\pi) = 3 \sin [2(t + \frac{1}{4}\pi)],$$

the graph is the curve $y = 3 \sin 2t$ displaced $\frac{1}{4}\pi$ units to the left.

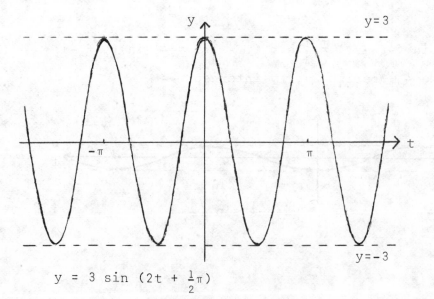

$$y = 3 \sin (2t + \frac{1}{2}\pi)$$

24. amplitude 2, period $\frac{8}{3}\pi$, y-intercept 0

Since

$$2 \sin \left(\frac{3}{4}t + \pi\right) = 2 \sin \left[\frac{3}{4}\left(t + \frac{4}{3}\pi\right)\right],$$

the graph is the curve $y = 2 \sin \frac{3}{4}t$ displaced $\frac{4}{3}\pi$ units to the left.

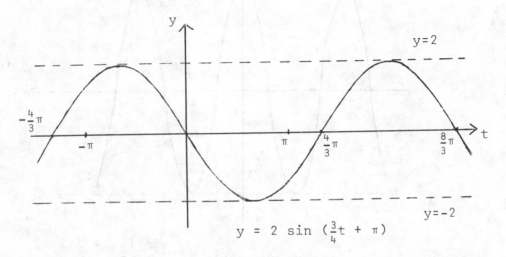

$$y = 2 \sin \left(\frac{3}{4}t + \pi\right)$$

25. amplitude 1, period π, y-intercept $\frac{1}{2}\sqrt{2}$

Since

$$\cos \left(2t + \frac{1}{4}\pi\right) = \cos \left[2\left(t + \frac{1}{8}\pi\right)\right],$$

the graph is the curve $y = \cos 2t$ displaced $\frac{1}{8}\pi$ units to the left.

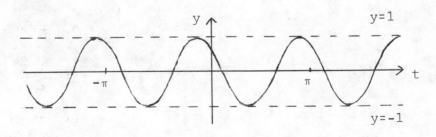

$$y = \cos \left(2t + \frac{1}{4}\pi\right)$$

26. $y = 3 \sin (\frac{5}{2}\pi - 2t) = -3 \sin (2t - \frac{5}{2}\pi) = 3 \sin (2t + \frac{1}{2}\pi)$

amplitude 3, period π, y-intercept 3

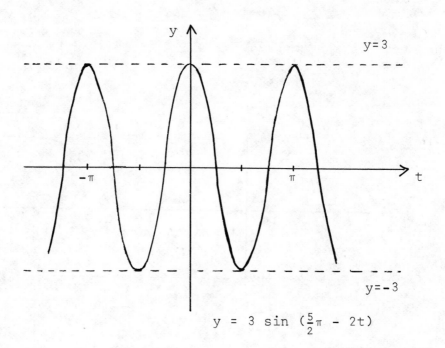

$$y = 3 \sin (\frac{5}{2}\pi - 2t)$$

SECTION 6.8

1. 1	2. -1	3. 0	4. $\frac{1}{3}\sqrt{3}$
5. -1	6. 1	7. $-\frac{1}{3}\sqrt{3}$	8. $-\sqrt{3}$
9. $-\sqrt{3}$	10. $\sqrt{3}$	11. 1	12. $\frac{1}{3}\sqrt{3}$
13. $-\sqrt{3}$	14. -1	15. $\frac{1}{3}\sqrt{3}$	16. $\frac{2}{3}\sqrt{3}$
17. 2	18. $\sqrt{2}$	19. -1	20. -2

21. $-\sqrt{2}$ 22. 2   23. $\frac{2}{3}\sqrt{3}$ 24. $\sqrt{2}$

25. 1   26. 1   27. $-\frac{2}{3}\sqrt{3}$ 28. $\frac{1}{2}\pi$

29. 2π 30. $\frac{1}{3}\pi$ 31. 3π 32. 1

33. 4   34. π 35. 2   36. 4

37. the lines $x = \pm\dfrac{2n+1}{2}\pi$ 38. the lines $x = \pm n\pi$

39. (a) for all numbers t for which sec t is defined,
       either sec t $\leq$ -1 or sec t $\geq$ 1

    (b) for all numbers t for which cosec t is defined,
       either cosec t $\leq$ -1 or cosec t $\geq$ 1

40. $-$ sec t   41. $-$ cosec t   42. cosec t   43. $-$ tan t

44. $-$ sec t   45. $-$ tan t

46. (a) $\tan^2 t + 1 = \sec^2 t$ (b) $\cot^2 t + 1 = \csc^2 t$

47. $\frac{1}{2}\pi$ 48. 2π 49. $\frac{1}{3}\pi$ 50. 3π

51. 1   52. 4   53. π 54. 2

55. 8

56.

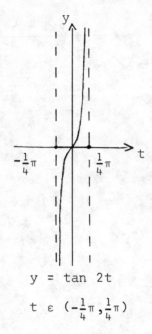

$$y = \tan 2t$$

$$t \ \varepsilon \ (-\tfrac{1}{4}\pi, \tfrac{1}{4}\pi)$$

57.

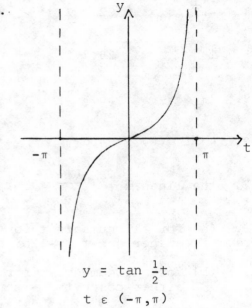

$$y = \tan \tfrac{1}{2}t$$

$$t \ \varepsilon \ (-\pi, \pi)$$

58.

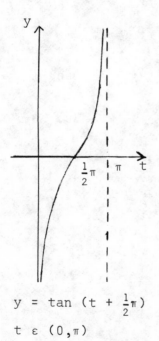

$$y = \tan (t + \tfrac{1}{2}\pi)$$

$$t \ \varepsilon \ (0, \pi)$$

59.

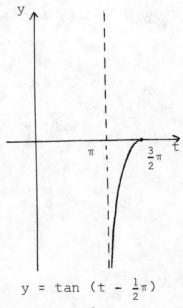

$$y = \tan (t - \tfrac{1}{2}\pi)$$

$$t \ \varepsilon \ (\pi, \ \tfrac{3}{2}\pi]$$

60.

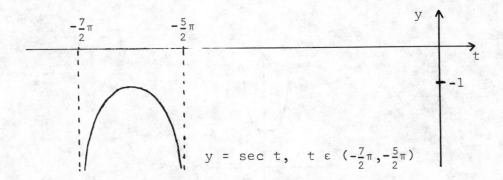

$$y = \sec t, \quad t \in (-\tfrac{7}{2}\pi, -\tfrac{5}{2}\pi)$$

61.

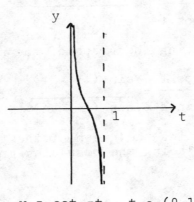

$$y = \cot \pi t, \quad t \in (0,1)$$

62.

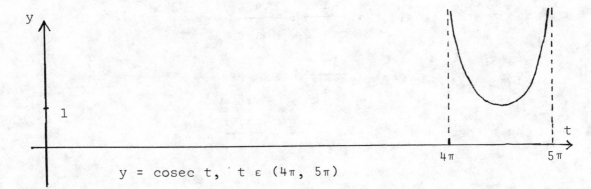

$$y = \operatorname{cosec} t, \quad t \in (4\pi, 5\pi)$$

63.

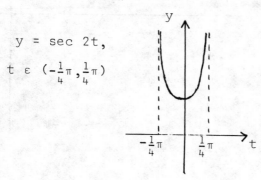

$$y = \sec 2t,$$

$$t \, \varepsilon \, (-\tfrac{1}{4}\pi, \tfrac{1}{4}\pi)$$

64. (a) $\sec t = \dfrac{1}{\cos t} = \dfrac{1}{\sin (t + \frac{1}{2}\pi)} = \operatorname{cosec} (t + \tfrac{1}{2}\pi)$

(b) by displacing the graph of the secant $\frac{1}{2}\pi$ units left

65. (a) $\cot t = \dfrac{\cos t}{\sin t} = \dfrac{\sin (\frac{1}{2}\pi - t)}{\cos (\frac{1}{2}\pi - t)} = \tan (\tfrac{1}{2}\pi - t)$

(b) by reflecting the graph of the tangent in the y-axis and then displacing the resulting graph $\frac{1}{2}\pi$ units to the left

SECTION 6.9

1. $\sin t \cot t = \sin t \cdot \dfrac{\cos t}{\sin t} = \cos t$

2. $\sin t \sec t = \sin t \cdot \dfrac{1}{\cos t} = \dfrac{\sin t}{\cos t} = \tan t$

3. $\cos t \tan t = \cos t \cdot \dfrac{\sin t}{\cos t} = \sin t$

4. $\cos t \operatorname{cosec} t = \cos t \cdot \dfrac{1}{\sin t} = \dfrac{\cos t}{\sin t} = \cot t$

5. $\cot t \sec t = \dfrac{\cos t}{\sin t} \cdot \dfrac{1}{\cos t} = \dfrac{1}{\sin t} = \operatorname{cosec} t$

6. $\tan t \operatorname{cosec} t = \dfrac{\sin t}{\cos t} \cdot \dfrac{1}{\sin t} = \dfrac{1}{\cos t} = \sec t$

7. $\tan^2 t \operatorname{cosec}^2 t = \dfrac{\sin^2 t}{\cos^2 t} \cdot \dfrac{1}{\sin^2 t} = \dfrac{1}{\cos^2 t} = \sec^2 t = \tan^2 t + 1$

$\qquad\qquad\qquad\qquad\qquad\qquad\qquad\qquad\qquad\qquad\qquad\uparrow$
$\qquad\qquad\qquad\qquad\qquad\qquad\qquad\qquad\qquad\qquad\quad (6.9.1)$

8. $\cot^2 t \sec^2 t = \dfrac{\cos^2 t}{\sin^2 t} \cdot \dfrac{1}{\cos^2 t} = \dfrac{1}{\sin^2 t} = \operatorname{cosec}^2 t = \cot^2 t + 1$

$\qquad\qquad\qquad\qquad\qquad\qquad\qquad\qquad\qquad\qquad\qquad\uparrow$
$\qquad\qquad\qquad\qquad\qquad\qquad\qquad\qquad\qquad\qquad\quad (6.9.1)$

9. $\cos^2 t \,(1 + \tan^2 t) = \cos^2 t \cdot \sec^2 t = \cos^2 t \cdot \dfrac{1}{\cos^2 t} = 1$

$\qquad\qquad\qquad\qquad\uparrow$
$\qquad\qquad\qquad\qquad\quad (6.9.1)$

10. $\operatorname{cosec}^2 t - \cot^2 t = \dfrac{1}{\sin^2 t} - \dfrac{\cos^2 t}{\sin^2 t} = \dfrac{1 - \cos^2 t}{\sin^2 t} = \dfrac{\sin^2 t}{\sin^2 t} = 1$

11. $\cos t + \tan t \sin t = \cos t + \dfrac{\sin t}{\cos t} \cdot \sin t$

$\qquad\qquad\qquad\qquad = \dfrac{\cos^2 t + \sin^2 t}{\cos t} = \dfrac{1}{\cos t} = \sec t$

12. $\cos t \,(\tan t + \cot t) = \cos t \left(\dfrac{\sin t}{\cos t} + \dfrac{\cos t}{\sin t} \right)$

$\qquad\qquad\qquad\qquad = \sin t + \dfrac{\cos^2 t}{\sin t}$

$\qquad\qquad\qquad\qquad = \dfrac{\sin^2 t + \cos^2 t}{\sin t} = \dfrac{1}{\sin t} = \operatorname{cosec} t$

13. $\sin t \,(\sec t + \cot t) = \sin t \left(\dfrac{1}{\cos t} + \dfrac{\cos t}{\sin t} \right)$

$\qquad\qquad\qquad\qquad = \dfrac{\sin t}{\cos t} + \cos t = \tan t + \cos t$

14. $\cosec t \, (1 + \tan t) = \dfrac{1}{\sin t} \left(1 + \dfrac{\sin t}{\cos t}\right)$

$\qquad\qquad\qquad\quad = \dfrac{1}{\sin t} + \dfrac{1}{\cos t}$

$\qquad\qquad\qquad\quad = \cosec t + \sec t = \sec t + \cosec t$

15. $\sin^4 t - \cos^4 t = (\sin^2 t + \cos^2 t)(\sin^2 t - \cos^2 t)$

$\qquad\qquad\qquad = 1 \cdot (\sin^2 t - \cos^2 t) = \sin^2 t - \cos^2 t$

16. $1 - 2\sin^2 t = 1 - 2(1 - \cos^2 t) = 1 - 2 + 2\cos^2 t = 2\cos^2 t - 1$

17. $\tan^2 t - \sin^2 t = \dfrac{\sin^2 t}{\cos^2 t} - \sin^2 t$

$\qquad\qquad\qquad = \sin^2 t \left(\dfrac{1}{\cos^2 t} - 1\right)$

$\qquad\qquad\qquad = \sin^2 t \,(\sec^2 t - 1) = \sin^2 t \,\tan^2 t = \tan^2 t + \sin^2 t$

18. $\sec^2 t + \cosec^2 t = \dfrac{1}{\cos^2 t} + \dfrac{1}{\sin^2 t}$

$\qquad\qquad\qquad = \dfrac{\sin^2 t + \cos^2 t}{\cos^2 t \, \sin^2 t}$

$\qquad\qquad\qquad = \dfrac{1}{\cos^2 t \, \sin^2 t} = \dfrac{1}{\cos^2 t} \cdot \dfrac{1}{\sin^2 t} = \sec^2 t \, \cosec^2 t$

19. $(\cot t - \cosec t)^6 (\cot t + \cosec t)^6 = (\cot^2 t - \cosec^2 t)^6 = 1^6 = 1$

20. $1 + (1 - \sin^2 t)(1 + \cot^2 t) = 1 + \cos^2 t \left(1 + \dfrac{\cos^2 t}{\sin^2 t}\right)$

$\qquad\qquad\qquad\qquad = 1 + \dfrac{\cos^2 t}{\sin^2 t} (\sin^2 t + \cos^2 t)$

$\qquad\qquad\qquad\qquad = 1 + \cot^2 t \cdot 1 = 1 + \cot^2 t = \cosec^2 t$

21. $\tan^4 t + \tan^2 t = \tan^2 t \,(\tan^2 t + 1)$

$\qquad\qquad\qquad = \tan^2 t \cdot \sec^2 t$

$\qquad\qquad\qquad = (\sec^2 t - 1)\,\sec^2 t = \sec^4 t - \sec^2 t$

22. $\cot^4 t + \cot^2 t = \cot^2 t \,(\cot^2 t + 1)$

$\qquad\qquad\qquad = \cot^2 t \cdot \csc^2 t$

$\qquad\qquad\qquad = (\csc^2 t - 1)\,\csc^2 t = \csc^4 t - \csc^2 t$

23. $\dfrac{\tan t - \cot t}{\sin t \cos t} = \dfrac{\dfrac{\sin t}{\cos t} - \dfrac{\cos t}{\sin t}}{\sin t \cos t} = \dfrac{1}{\cos^2 t} - \dfrac{1}{\sin^2 t}$

$\qquad\qquad\qquad\qquad = \sec^2 t - \csc^2 t$

24. $\dfrac{\tan t + \sin t}{1 + \sec t} = \dfrac{\dfrac{\sin t}{\cos t} + \sin t}{1 + \dfrac{1}{\cos t}} = \dfrac{\sin t \left(\dfrac{1}{\cos t} + 1\right)}{1 + \dfrac{1}{\cos t}} = \sin t$

25. $\dfrac{1 - \sin t}{\cos t} = \dfrac{1 - \sin t}{\cos t} \cdot \dfrac{1 + \sin t}{1 + \sin t}$

$\qquad\quad = \dfrac{1 - \sin^2 t}{\cos t} \cdot \dfrac{1}{1 + \sin t}$

$\qquad\quad = \dfrac{\cos^2 t}{\cos t} \cdot \dfrac{1}{1 + \sin t} = \cos t \cdot \dfrac{1}{1 + \sin t} = \dfrac{\cos t}{1 + \sin t}$

26. $\dfrac{\tan^2 t - 1}{\tan^2 t + 1} = \dfrac{\dfrac{\sin^2 t}{\cos^2 t} - 1}{\dfrac{\sin^2 t}{\cos^2 t} + 1} = \dfrac{\sin^2 t - \cos^2 t}{\sin^2 t + \cos^2 t} = \dfrac{\sin^2 t - \cos^2 t}{1}$

$$= \sin^2 t - \cos^2 t$$

27. $\dfrac{\cos t}{1 - \sin t} = \dfrac{\cos t}{1 - \sin t}\left(\dfrac{1 + \sin t}{1 + \sin t}\right)$

$$= \dfrac{\cos t}{1 - \sin^2 t}\,(1 + \sin t)$$

$$= \dfrac{\cos t}{\cos^2 t}\,(1 + \sin t)$$

$$= \dfrac{1}{\cos t}\,(1 + \sin t)$$

$$= \dfrac{1}{\cos t} + \dfrac{\sin t}{\cos t} = \sec t + \tan t = \tan t + \sec t$$

28. $\dfrac{1 - \sin t}{1 + \sin t} = \dfrac{1 - \sin t}{1 + \sin t} \cdot \dfrac{1 - \sin t}{1 - \sin t}$

$$= \dfrac{1 - 2\sin t + \sin^2 t}{1 - \sin^2 t}$$

$$= \dfrac{1 - 2\sin t + \sin^2 t}{\cos^2 t}$$

$$= \dfrac{1}{\cos^2 t} - 2\left(\dfrac{1}{\cos t}\right)\left(\dfrac{\sin t}{\cos t}\right) + \dfrac{\sin^2 t}{\cos^2 t}$$

$$= \sec^2 t - 2\sec t \tan t + \tan^2 t = (\sec t - \tan t)^2$$

29. $\dfrac{\sin t - \cos t}{\sin t + \cos t} = \dfrac{\dfrac{\sin t}{\sin t \cos t} - \dfrac{\cos t}{\sin t \cos t}}{\dfrac{\sin t}{\sin t \cos t} + \dfrac{\cos t}{\sin t \cos t}}$

$= \dfrac{\dfrac{1}{\cos t} - \dfrac{1}{\sin t}}{\dfrac{1}{\cos t} + \dfrac{1}{\sin t}} = \dfrac{\sec t - \csc t}{\sec t + \csc t}$

30. $\dfrac{\tan t + 1}{\tan t - 1} = \dfrac{\dfrac{\tan t}{\tan t} + \dfrac{1}{\tan t}}{\dfrac{\tan t}{\tan t} - \dfrac{1}{\tan t}} = \dfrac{1 + \cot t}{1 - \cot t}$

31. $\dfrac{\sin^3 t - \cos^3 t}{\sin t - \cos t} = \sin^2 t + \sin t \cos t + \cos^2 t$

$= (\cos^2 t + \sin^2 t) + \sin t \cos t = 1 + \sin t \cos t$

32. $\dfrac{\sin^3 t + \cos^3 t}{\sin t + \cos t} = \sin^2 t - \sin t \cos t + \cos^2 t$

$= (\cos^2 t + \sin^2 t) - \sin t \cos t = 1 - \sin t \cos t$

33. $\dfrac{1}{\csc t + 1} + \dfrac{1}{\csc t - 1} = \dfrac{(\csc t - 1) + (\csc t + 1)}{(\csc t + 1)(\csc t - 1)}$

$= \dfrac{2 \csc t}{\csc^2 t - 1} = \dfrac{2 \dfrac{1}{\sin t}}{\dfrac{1}{\sin^2 t} - 1}$

(over)

$$= \frac{\dfrac{2}{\sin t}}{\dfrac{1 - \sin^2 t}{\sin^2 t}} = \frac{\dfrac{2}{\sin t}}{\dfrac{\cos^2 t}{\sin^2 t}} = \frac{2}{\sin t} \cdot \frac{\sin^2 t}{\cos^2 t} = 2 \frac{\sin t}{\cos t} \cdot \frac{1}{\cos t}$$

$$= 2 \tan t \sec t$$

34.
$$\frac{\sin t - \cos t}{\cos^2 t} = \frac{\sin t - \cos t}{\cos^2 t} \cdot \frac{\sin t + \cos t}{\sin t + \cos t}$$

$$= \frac{\sin^2 t - \cos^2 t}{\cos^2 t \, (\sin t + \cos t)}$$

$$= \frac{\dfrac{\sin^2 t}{\cos^2 t} - 1}{\sin t + \cos t} = \frac{\tan^2 t - 1}{\sin t + \cos t}$$

SECTION 6.10

1. $\cos \frac{1}{8}\pi = \frac{1}{2}\sqrt{2 + \sqrt{2}}, \quad \sin \frac{1}{8}\pi = \frac{1}{2}\sqrt{2 - \sqrt{2}}, \quad \tan \frac{1}{8}\pi = \sqrt{2} - 1$

2. $\cos \frac{3}{8}\pi = \frac{1}{2}\sqrt{2 - \sqrt{2}}, \quad \sin \frac{3}{8}\pi = \frac{1}{2}\sqrt{2 + \sqrt{2}}, \quad \tan \frac{3}{8}\pi = \sqrt{2} + 1$

3. $\cos \frac{5}{8}\pi = -\frac{1}{2}\sqrt{2 - \sqrt{2}}, \quad \sin \frac{5}{8}\pi = \frac{1}{2}\sqrt{2 + \sqrt{2}}, \quad \tan \frac{5}{8}\pi = -1 - \sqrt{2}$

4. $\cos \frac{7}{8}\pi = -\frac{1}{2}\sqrt{2 + \sqrt{2}}, \quad \sin \frac{7}{8}\pi = \frac{1}{2}\sqrt{2 - \sqrt{2}}, \quad \tan \frac{7}{8}\pi = 1 - \sqrt{2}$

5. $\cos \frac{9}{8}\pi = -\frac{1}{2}\sqrt{2 + \sqrt{2}}, \quad \sin \frac{9}{8}\pi = -\frac{1}{2}\sqrt{2 - \sqrt{2}}, \quad \tan \frac{9}{8}\pi = \sqrt{2} - 1$

6. $\cos \frac{11}{8}\pi = -\frac{1}{2}\sqrt{2 - \sqrt{2}}, \quad \sin \frac{11}{8}\pi = -\frac{1}{2}\sqrt{2 + \sqrt{2}}, \quad \tan \frac{11}{8}\pi = \sqrt{2} + 1$

7. $\cos \frac{13}{8}\pi = \frac{1}{2}\sqrt{2 - \sqrt{2}}, \quad \sin \frac{13}{8}\pi = -\frac{1}{2}\sqrt{2 + \sqrt{2}}, \quad \tan \frac{13}{8}\pi = -1 - \sqrt{2}$

8. $\cos \frac{15}{8}\pi = \frac{1}{2}\sqrt{2 + \sqrt{2}}, \quad \sin \frac{15}{8}\pi = -\frac{1}{2}\sqrt{2 - \sqrt{2}}, \quad \tan \frac{15}{8}\pi = 1 - \sqrt{2}$

9. $\begin{aligned}
\sin (s + t) &= \cos [\tfrac{1}{2}\pi - (s + t)] \\
&= \cos [(\tfrac{1}{2}\pi - s) - t] \\
&= \cos (\tfrac{1}{2}\pi - s) \cos t + \sin (\tfrac{1}{2}\pi - s) \sin t \\
&= \sin s \cos t + \cos s \sin t
\end{aligned}$

10. $\begin{aligned}
\sin (s - t) &= \sin [s + (-t)] \\
&= \sin s \cos (-t) + \cos s \sin (-t) \\
&= \sin s \cos t + \cos s (- \sin t) \\
&= \sin s \cos t - \cos s \sin t
\end{aligned}$

11. (a) $\tan \tfrac{1}{2}t \underset{(6.10.7)}{=} \dfrac{\sin t}{1 + \cos t} = \dfrac{\sin t}{1 + \cos t} \cdot \dfrac{1 - \cos t}{1 - \cos t}$

$\qquad\qquad = \dfrac{\sin t (1 - \cos t)}{1 - \cos^2 t}$

$\qquad\qquad = \dfrac{\sin t (1 - \cos t)}{\sin^2 t} = \dfrac{1 - \cos t}{\sin t}$

(b) $\tan \tfrac{1}{12}\pi = 2 - \sqrt{3}$

12. $\dfrac{1 + \cos t}{\sin t} \quad \text{or} \quad \dfrac{\sin t}{1 - \cos t}$

13. if $\sin t = 0$, then $\sin 2t = 2 \sin t \cos t = 2(0) \cos t = 0$;

if $\cos t = 0$, then $\sin t = \pm 1$ and $\cos 2t = \cos^2 t - \sin^2 t$

$\qquad\qquad\qquad\qquad\qquad\qquad = 0 - 1 = -1$

14. no; $\sin \pi = 0$ but $\sin \frac{1}{2}\pi = 1 \neq 0$

15. $\cot (s+t) = \dfrac{\cot s \cot t - 1}{\cot s + \cot t}$, $\cot (s-t) = -\dfrac{\cot s \cot t + 1}{\cot s - \cot t}$

$$\cot (s+t) = \frac{1}{\tan (s+t)}$$

$$= \frac{1 - \tan s \tan t}{\tan s + \tan t} = \frac{\dfrac{1}{\tan s \tan t} - 1}{\dfrac{1}{\tan t} + \dfrac{1}{\tan s}}$$

$$= \frac{\cot s \cot t - 1}{\cot t + \cot s}$$

$$= \frac{\cot s \cot t - 1}{\cot s + \cot t}$$

16. $\dfrac{3}{5}$

17. $-\dfrac{7}{25}$

18. $\dfrac{24}{25}$

19. $\dfrac{4}{3}$

20. $-\dfrac{24}{7}$

21. $\dfrac{1}{5}\sqrt{5}$

22. $\dfrac{2}{5}\sqrt{5}$

23. $\dfrac{2}{25}\sqrt{5}$

24. $-\dfrac{3}{5}$

25. $\dfrac{24}{25}$

26. $\dfrac{7}{25}$

27. $\dfrac{3}{4}$

28. $-\dfrac{1}{10}\sqrt{10}$

29. $\dfrac{24}{7}$

30. $\dfrac{3}{10}\sqrt{10}$

31. -3

32. $-\dfrac{12}{13}$

33. $-\dfrac{5}{13}$

34. $\dfrac{120}{119}$

35. $\dfrac{119}{169}$

36. $\dfrac{120}{169}$

37. -5

38. $\dfrac{5}{26}\sqrt{26}$

39. $-\dfrac{828}{2197}$

40. $\cos(s+t) + \cos(s-t) = (\cos s \cos t - \sin s \sin t)$

$$+ (\cos s \cos t + \sin s \sin t)$$

$$= 2 \cos s \cos t$$

$\sin(s+t) - \sin(s-t) = (\sin s \cos t + \cos s \sin t)$

$$- (\sin s \cos t - \cos s \sin t)$$

$$= 2 \cos s \sin t$$

$-\cos(s+t) + \cos(s-t) = (-\cos s \cos t + \sin s \sin t)$

$$+ (\cos s \cos t + \sin s \sin t)$$

$$= 2 \sin s \sin t$$

41. $\cos 3t + \cos t$ 42. $\sin 3t + \sin t$ 43. $\cos t - \cos 3t$

44. by the first identity of (6.10.8)

$$2 \cos \frac{s+t}{2} \cos \frac{s-t}{2} = \cos \left(\frac{s+t}{2} + \frac{s-t}{2} \right) + \cos \left(\frac{s+t}{2} - \frac{s-t}{2} \right)$$

$$= \cos s + \cos t;$$

by the third identity of (6.10.8)

$$-2 \sin \frac{s+t}{2} \sin \frac{s-t}{2} = \cos \left(\frac{s+t}{2} + \frac{s-t}{2} \right) - \cos \left(\frac{s+t}{2} - \frac{s-t}{2} \right)$$

$$= \cos s - \cos t;$$

by the second identity of (6.10.8)

$$2 \sin \frac{s+t}{2} \cos \frac{s-t}{2} = 2 \cos \frac{s-t}{2} \sin \frac{s+t}{2}$$

$$= \sin \left(\frac{s-t}{2} + \frac{s+t}{2} \right) - \sin \left(\frac{s-t}{2} - \frac{s+t}{2} \right)$$

$$= \sin s - \sin(-t) = \sin s + \sin t;$$

by the second identity of (6.10.8)

$$2 \cos \frac{s+t}{2} \sin \frac{s-t}{2} = \sin \left(\frac{s+t}{2} + \frac{s-t}{2}\right) - \sin \left(\frac{s+t}{2} - \frac{s-t}{2}\right)$$

$$= \sin s - \sin t.$$

45. $\frac{1}{2}\pi$, $\frac{7}{6}\pi$, $\frac{3}{2}\pi$, $\frac{11}{6}\pi$

46. $\frac{1}{3}\pi$, $\frac{2}{3}\pi$, $\frac{4}{3}\pi$, $\frac{5}{3}\pi$

47. no real numbers satisfy this equation

48. $\frac{1}{8}\pi$, $\frac{5}{8}\pi$, $\frac{9}{8}\pi$, $\frac{13}{8}\pi$

49. $\frac{3}{8}\pi$, $\frac{7}{8}\pi$, $\frac{11}{8}\pi$, $\frac{15}{8}\pi$

50. 0, π, 2π

SECTION 6.11

1. 0

2. $\frac{1}{2}\pi$

3. $\frac{1}{3}\pi$

4. $\frac{1}{3}\pi$

5. $-\frac{1}{3}\pi$

6. $\frac{2}{3}\pi$

7. 0

8. $-\frac{1}{4}\pi$

9. $-\frac{1}{6}\pi$

10. $\frac{5}{6}\pi$

11. $\frac{1}{2}$

12. $-\frac{1}{4}\pi$

13. $-\frac{1}{4}\pi$

14. $-\frac{1}{6}\pi$

15. $\frac{1}{2}\sqrt{3}$

16. $\frac{1}{2}\sqrt{3}$

17. $\frac{1}{4}\pi$

18. $\frac{1}{4}\pi$

19. $\frac{1}{2}\sqrt{3}$

20. 0

21. 1.16

22. -0.92

23. -0.46

24. 1.26

25. 0.28

26. $\pi - 1.43$

27. $\dfrac{1}{\sqrt{1 + t^2}}$

28. $\dfrac{t}{\sqrt{1 + t^2}}$

29. t

30. $\dfrac{1}{t}$

31. $\sqrt{1 + t^2}$

32. $\dfrac{\sqrt{1 + t^2}}{t}$

33. $\sqrt{1 - t^2}$ 34. t 35. $\dfrac{1}{t}$ 36. $\dfrac{\sqrt{1 - t^2}}{t}$

37. $\dfrac{t}{\sqrt{1 - t^2}}$ 38. $\dfrac{1}{\sqrt{1 - t^2}}$

39. $g(t) = \cot^{-1} t$, t real; $f(t) = \cot t$, $t \, \varepsilon \, (0, \pi)$

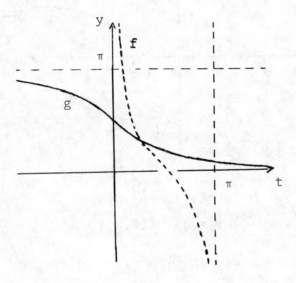

40. $g(t) = \sec^{-1} t, \quad t \in (-\infty, -1] \cup [1, \infty);$

   $f(t) = \sec t, \quad t \in [0, \tfrac{1}{2}\pi) \cup (\tfrac{1}{2}\pi, \pi]$

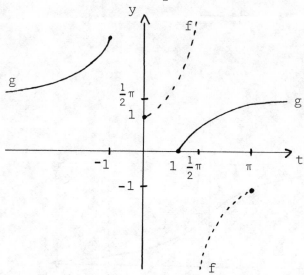

41. $g(t) = \operatorname{cosec}^{-1} t, \quad t \in (-\infty, 1] \cup [1, \infty);$

   $f(t) = \operatorname{cosec} t, \quad t \in [-\tfrac{1}{2}\pi, 0) \cup (0, \tfrac{1}{2}\pi]$

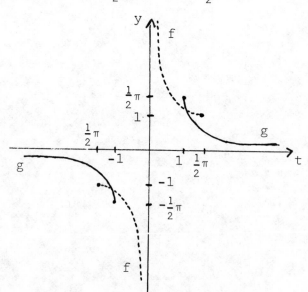

42. $\frac{1}{2}\pi$ 43. $\frac{1}{3}\pi$ 44. $\frac{1}{4}\pi$ 45. $\frac{3}{4}\pi$

46. $\frac{2}{3}\pi$ 47. $\frac{5}{6}\pi$ 48. $\dfrac{1}{t}$ 49. $\dfrac{\sqrt{t^2 - 1}}{t}$

50. $\sqrt{t^2 - 1}$ 51. $\dfrac{1}{\sqrt{t^2 - 1}}$ 52. t 53. $\dfrac{t}{\sqrt{t^2 - 1}}$

54. (a) For $t > 0$ we use the triangle.

$$\sin (2 \tan^{-1}t) = 2 \sin (\tan^{-1}t) \cos (\tan^{-1}t)$$

$$= 2 \, \frac{t}{\sqrt{1 + t^2}} \cdot \frac{1}{\sqrt{1 + t^2}}$$

$$= \frac{2t}{1 + t^2}.$$

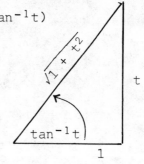

The result obviously holds at $t = 0$.

Suppose then that $t < 0$. Then $-t > 0$ and therefore

$$\sin (2 \tan^{-1}(-t)) = \frac{2(-t)}{1 + (-t)^2} = \frac{-2t}{1 + t^2}.$$

But, since the inverse tangent and the sine are both odd,

$$\sin (2 \tan^{-1}(-t)) = \sin (-2 \tan^{-1}t) = - \sin (2 \tan^{-1}t).$$

Thus we have

$$- \sin (2 \tan^{-1}t) = \frac{-2t}{1 + t^2}$$

and

$$\sin (2 \tan^{-1}t) = \frac{2t}{1 + t^2}$$

(b) For t > 0 we use the triangle.

$$\cos(2 \tan^{-1}t) = \cos^2(\tan^{-1}t) - \sin^2(\tan^{-1}t)$$

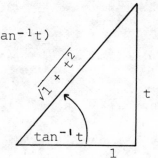

$$= \frac{1}{1 + t^2} - \frac{t^2}{1 + t^2}$$

$$= \frac{1 - t^2}{1 + t^2} .$$

The result obviously holds at t = 0.

Suppose then that t < 0. Then -t > 0 and therefore

$$\cos(2 \tan^{-1}(-t)) = \frac{1 - (-t)^2}{1 + (-t)^2} = \frac{1 - t^2}{1 + t^2} .$$

Since the inverse tangent is odd and the cosine is even,

$$\cos(2 \tan^{-1}(-t)) = \cos(-2 \tan^{-1}t) = \cos(2 \tan^{-1}t).$$

Thus

$$\cos(2 \tan^{-1}t) = \frac{1 - t^2}{1 + t^2} .$$

SECTION 6.12

1. (a) $\frac{3}{4}\pi$ (b) $\frac{5}{6}\pi$ (c) $\frac{3}{2}\pi$ (d) $\frac{11}{6}\pi$

2. (a) 30°   (b) 33.75°   (c) about 114.6°   (d) 112.50°

3. arc length 5π, area 10π 4. $\theta = \frac{1}{2}\sqrt{2}\pi$, area $\sqrt{2}\pi$

5. $\cos t = \frac{1}{4}$, $\sin t = \pm\sqrt{1 - \frac{1}{16}} = \pm\frac{1}{4}\sqrt{15}$, $\tan t = \frac{\sin t}{\cos t} = \pm\sqrt{15}$

6. (a) $\frac{1}{2}\sqrt{3}$ (b) $-\frac{1}{2}$ (c) $\frac{1}{2}\sqrt{3}$ (d) $\frac{1}{3}\sqrt{3}$

    (e) $-\sqrt{2}$ (f) 1 (g) $-\sqrt{3}$ (h) 2

7. (a) $\frac{1}{2}\sqrt{3}$ (b) π (c) $\frac{1}{2}\sqrt{3}$ (d) $\frac{1}{3}\pi$ (e) -1

    (f) $\frac{3}{5}$ (g) $-\frac{1}{3}\pi$ (h) $\frac{4}{5}$ (i) $\frac{4}{3}$

8. (a) $-\frac{17}{25}$ (b) $-\frac{4}{25}\sqrt{21}$ (c) $-\frac{1}{10}\sqrt{70}$ (d) $\frac{1}{10}\sqrt{30}$

9. (a) amplitude $\frac{1}{3}$, period π, y-intercept $\frac{1}{3}$

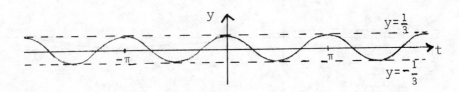

$$y = \frac{1}{3}\cos 2t$$

    (b) amplitude 2, period π, y-intercept -2

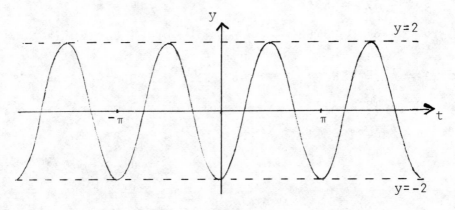

$$y = 2\cos(2t + \pi)$$

(c) amplitude $\frac{1}{2}$, period $\frac{1}{2}\pi$, y-intercept $\frac{1}{2}$

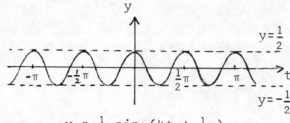

$$y = \frac{1}{2} \sin (4t + \frac{1}{2}\pi)$$

(d) amplitude $\frac{1}{4}$, period 4π, y-intercept $\frac{1}{8}\sqrt{2}$

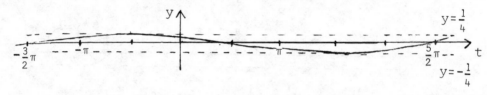

$$y = \frac{1}{4} \sin (\frac{1}{2}t - \frac{13}{4}\pi)$$

10. $\sin A = 0.6000, \quad A \cong 37°$

  $B \cong 90° - 37° = 53°$

  $b \cong 5 \cos 37° \cong 3.99$

11. $A = 90° - 80° \cong 10°$

  $a = 4 \sin 10° \cong 0.69$

  $b = 4 \cos 10° \cong 3.94$

12. $\cos A = \frac{10}{15} \cong 0.6667, \quad A \cong 48°$

  $B \cong 90° - 48° = 42°$

  $a = 15 \sin 48° \cong 11.15$

13. $B \cong 90° - 63° = 27°$

  $b = 9 \cot 63° = 9 \tan 27°$
  $\cong 4.59$

  $c = 9 \csc 63° = 9 \sec 27°$
  $\cong 10.10$

14. $B \cong 90° - 32° = 58°$

  $a = \tan 32° \cong 0.62$

  $c = \sec 32° \cong 1.18$

15. $\tan A = \frac{15}{25} = 0.6000, \quad A \cong 31°$

  $B \cong 90° - 31° = 59°$

  $c = 15 \csc 31°$
  $= 15 \sec 59° \cong 29.13$

16. $A = 180° - 80° - 70° = 30°$

   $b = 5 \sin 80° \ \text{cosec} \ 30° = 5 \sin 80° \sec 60° \cong 9.85$

   $c = 5 \sin 70° \ \text{cosec} \ 30° = 5 \sin 70° \sec 60° \cong 9.40$

17. $c^2 = 4 + 1 - 2(2)(1) \cos 60° = 3, \quad c = \sqrt{3} \cong 1.732$

   $A = 90°, \quad B = 30°$

18. $C = 180° - 30° - 75° = 75°$ (isoceles triangle)

   $b = 10, \quad a = 10 \sin 30° \ \text{cosec} \ 75° = 10 \sin 30° \sec 15° \cong 5.18$

19. $b^2 = 25 + 1 - 2(5)(1) \cos 63° \cong 21.46, \quad b \cong 4.63$

   $25 = 21.46 + 1 - 2(4.63)(1) \cos A, \quad \cos A \cong -0.2743, \quad A \cong 106°$

   $C \cong 180° - 106° - 63° = 11°$

20. $100 = 121 + 144 - 2(11)(12) \cos A, \quad \cos A \cong 0.6250, \quad A \cong 51°$

   $121 = 100 + 144 - 2(10)(12) \cos B, \quad \cos B \cong 0.5125, \quad B \cong 59°$

   $C \cong 180° - 51° - 59° = 70°$

21. $B = 180° - 40° - 60° = 80°$

   $a = 12 \sin 40° \ \text{cosec} \ 80° = 12 \sin 40° \sec 10° \cong 7.83$

   $c = 12 \sin 60° \ \text{cosec} \ 80° = 12 \sin 60° \sec 10° \cong 10.55$

22. $a^2 = 9 + 4 - 2(3)(2) \cos 40° \cong 3.81, \quad a \cong 1.95$

   $9 = 3.81 + 4 - 2(1.95)(2) \cos B, \quad \cos B \cong -0.1526, \quad B \cong 99°$

   $C \cong 180° - 40° - 99° = 41°$

23. $4 = 16 + 25 - 2(4)(5) \cos A$, $\cos A = 0.9250$, $A \cong 22°$

$16 = 4 + 25 - 2(2)(5) \cos B$, $\cos B = 0.6500$, $B \cong 49°$

$C \cong 180° - 22° - 49° = 109°$

24. $S = 4 \sin 6° \cong 0.42$ (about 0.42 miles south)

$E = 4 \cos 6° \cong 3.98$ (about 3.98 miles east)

25. (a) $h = 10 \tan 32° \cong 6.249$
        (about 6.25 ft; namely
         about 6 ft, 3 in)

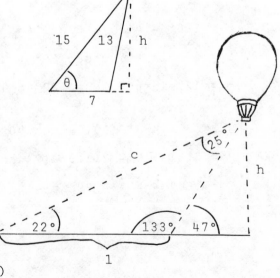

(b) $h = 10 \sin 32° \operatorname{cosec} 68° = 10 \sin 32° \sec 22° \cong 5.72$
        (about 5.72 ft, which is a little less than 5 ft, 9 in)

26. $169 = 49 + 225 - 2(7)(15) \cos \theta$

$\cos \theta = 0.5000$

$\theta = 60°$

$h = 15 \sin 60°$

$= \dfrac{15}{2}\sqrt{3} \cong 12.99$

27. $c = \sin 133° \operatorname{cosec} 25°$

$= \sin 47° \sec 65° \cong 1.73$

$h = c \sin 22°$

$\cong 1.73 \sin 22° \cong 0.65$

(about 0.65 miles high;
 that is, about 3432 ft high)

28. about 60 mph   (1050 inches per second)

29. $\tan 30° = \dfrac{h}{d-1}$,

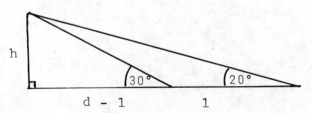

$\tan 20° = \dfrac{h}{d}$

$(d-1)\tan 30° = h = d\tan 20°$

$d(\tan 30° - \tan 20°) = \tan 30°$

$$d = \frac{\tan 30°}{\tan 30° - \tan 20°}$$

$$h = d\tan 20° = \frac{\tan 30° \; \tan 20°}{\tan 30° - \tan 20°} \cong 0.98$$

(about 0.98 miles high)

30. $\sin \frac{1}{2}A = \frac{1}{4} = 0.2500$

$\frac{1}{2}A \cong 14.5°, \quad A \cong 29°$

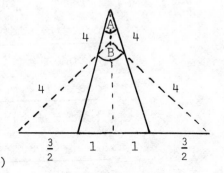

$\sin \frac{1}{2}B = \dfrac{1 + \frac{3}{2}}{4} = 0.6250$

$\frac{1}{2}B \cong 39°, \quad B \cong 78°$

$B - A \cong 49°$ (about 49° wider)

31. $\dfrac{\sin 2t}{1 + \cos 2t} = \dfrac{2\sin t \cos t}{1 + \cos^2 t - \sin^2 t}$

$ = \dfrac{2\sin t \cos t}{(1 - \sin^2 t) + \cos^2 t}$

$ = \dfrac{2\sin t \cos t}{\cos^2 t + \cos^2 t} = \dfrac{2\sin t \cos t}{2\cos^2 t} = \dfrac{\sin t}{\cos t} = \tan t$

32. $\cos t \cos 2t + \sin t \sin 2t = \cos t (\cos^2 t - \sin^2 t)$

$$+ \sin t (2 \sin t \cos t)$$

$$= \cos^3 t - \cos t \sin^2 t$$

$$+ 2 \cos t \sin^2 t$$

$$= \cos^3 t + \cos t \sin^2 t$$

$$= \cos t (\cos^2 t + \sin^2 t)$$

$$= \cos t \cdot 1 = \cos t$$

33. $$\frac{1}{\csc t + \cot t} = \frac{1}{\dfrac{1}{\sin t} + \dfrac{\cos t}{\sin t}} = \frac{1}{\dfrac{1 + \cos t}{\sin t}} = \frac{\sin t}{1 + \cos t}$$

$$= \tan \tfrac{1}{2} t$$

$$\underset{\uparrow}{} \quad (6.10.7)$$

34. $$\frac{1 + \sin 2t}{\cos 2t} = \frac{1 + 2 \sin t \cos t}{\cos^2 t - \sin^2 t}$$

$$= \frac{(\cos^2 t + \sin^2 t) + 2 \sin t \cos t}{(\cos t + \sin t)(\cos t - \sin t)}$$

$$= \frac{\cos^2 t + 2 \cos t \sin t + \sin^2 t}{(\cos t + \sin t)(\cos t - \sin t)}$$

$$= \frac{(\cos t + \sin t)^2}{(\cos t + \sin t)(\cos t - \sin t)} = \frac{\cos t + \sin t}{\cos t - \sin t}$$

35. $\sin 3t = 3 \sin t - 4 \sin^3 t$

36. $\cos 3t = 4 \cos^3 t - 3 \cos t$

37. $\sin 4t = 4 \cos^3 t \sin t - 4 \sin^3 t \cos t$

$$= 8 \cos^3 t \sin t - 4 \cos t \sin t$$

38. $\cos 4t = 8\cos^4 t - 8\cos^2 t + 1$

39. $0, \frac{2}{3}\pi, \pi, \frac{4}{3}\pi, 2\pi$

40. $\frac{1}{3}\pi, \pi, \frac{5}{3}\pi$

41. $\frac{2}{3}\pi, \pi, \frac{4}{3}\pi$

42. $0, \frac{1}{4}\pi, \frac{3}{4}\pi, \pi, \frac{5}{4}\pi, \frac{7}{4}\pi, 2\pi$

43. $\frac{1}{2}\pi$

44. angular velocity of $P_1 = \dfrac{2\pi}{t_1}$, angular velocity of $P_2 = \dfrac{2\pi}{t_2}$

    If t is the time between sucessive eclipses, then

    (difference in angular velocities)t = 2π

    $$\left(\frac{2\pi}{t_1} - \frac{2\pi}{t_2}\right)t = 2\pi$$

    $$t = \frac{1}{\dfrac{1}{t_1} - \dfrac{1}{t_2}} = \frac{t_1 t_2}{t_2 - t_1}$$

45. $\cos(t + 2\pi) = \cos\left[\dfrac{180}{\pi}(t + 2\pi)\right]° = \cos\left(\dfrac{180}{\pi}t° + 360°\right)$

    same steps give the second identity $= \cos\left(\dfrac{180}{\pi}t\right)° = \cos t$

46. $\cos(t + \pi) = \cos\left[\dfrac{180}{\pi}(t + \pi)\right]° = \cos\left(\dfrac{180}{\pi}t° + 180°\right)$

    same steps give the second identity $= -\cos\left(\dfrac{180}{\pi}t\right)° = -\cos t$

47. $\cos(\pi - t) = \cos\left[\dfrac{180}{\pi}(\pi - t)\right]° = \cos\left(180° - \dfrac{180}{\pi}t°\right)$

    $$= -\cos\left(\dfrac{180}{\pi}t\right)° = -\cos t$$

$$\sin (\pi - t) = \sin [\frac{180}{\pi} (\pi - t)]° = \sin (180° - \frac{180}{\pi} t°)$$

$$= \sin (\frac{180}{\pi} t)° = \sin t$$

48. $\dfrac{1}{\sqrt{1 + t^2}}$ 49. $\dfrac{t}{\sqrt{1 + t^2}}$ 50. t

51. $\dfrac{1}{t}$ 52. $\sqrt{1 + t^2}$ 53. $\dfrac{\sqrt{1 + t^2}}{t}$

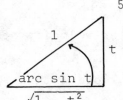   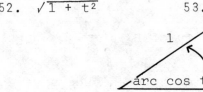

54. $\sin (2 \text{ arc sin } t) = 2 \sin (\text{arc sin } t) \cos (\text{arc sin } t)$

$$= 2t\sqrt{1 - t^2}$$

55. $\cos (2 \text{ arc sin } t) = \cos^2(\text{arc sin } t) - \sin^2(\text{arc sin } t)$

$$= (1 - t^2) - (t^2) = 1 - 2t^2$$

56. $\sin (2 \text{ arc cos } t) = 2 \sin (\text{arc cos } t) \cos (\text{arc cos } t)$

$$= 2\sqrt{1 - t^2}\, t = 2t\sqrt{1 - t^2}$$

57. $\cos (2 \text{ arc cos } t) = \cos^2(\text{arc cos } t) - \sin^2(\text{arc cos } t)$

$$= t^2 - (1 - t^2) = 2t^2 - 1$$

58. $4 \sin \frac{1}{3}t \sin [\frac{1}{3}(\pi + t)] \sin [\frac{1}{3}(\pi - t)] =$

$$\underset{(6.10.8)}{=} (4 \sin \frac{1}{3}t) \frac{1}{2} (\cos \frac{2}{3}t - \cos \frac{2}{3}\pi)$$

$$= 2 \sin \frac{1}{3}t (\cos \frac{2}{3}t + \frac{1}{2})$$

$$= 2 \sin \frac{1}{3}t \cos \frac{2}{3}t + \sin \frac{1}{3}t$$

$$\underset{(6.10.8)}{=} \sin t + \sin (-\frac{1}{3}t) + \sin \frac{1}{3}t = \sin t$$

SECTION 7.2

1. $y^2 = 8x$

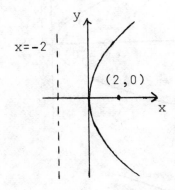

2. $y^2 = -8x$

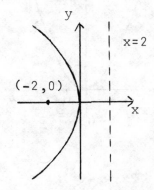

3. $x^2 = 8y$

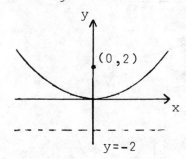

4. $x^2 = -8y$

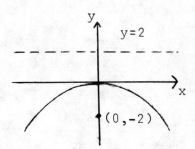

5. $y^2 = 2x$

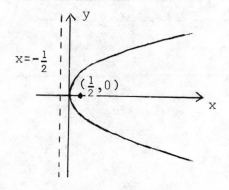

6. $x^2 = -2y$

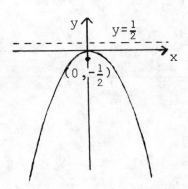

7. $x^2 = 2y$

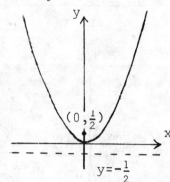

$(0, \frac{1}{2})$

$y = -\frac{1}{2}$

8. $y^2 = -2x$

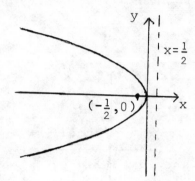

$x = \frac{1}{2}$

$(-\frac{1}{2}, 0)$

9. $y^2 = 2x = 4(\frac{1}{2})x$

$c = \frac{1}{2}, \quad F(\frac{1}{2}, 0)$

directrix $x = -\frac{1}{2}$

axis $y = 0$

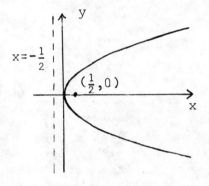

$x = -\frac{1}{2}$

$(\frac{1}{2}, 0)$

10. $x^2 = 5y = 4(\frac{5}{4})y$

$c = \frac{5}{4}, \quad F(0, \frac{5}{4})$

directrix $y = -\frac{5}{4}$

axis $x = 0$

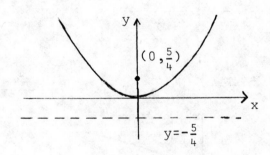

$(0, \frac{5}{4})$

$y = -\frac{5}{4}$

11. $x^2 = -3y = 4(-\frac{3}{4})y$

$c = -\frac{3}{4}, \quad F(0, -\frac{3}{4})$

directrix $y = \frac{3}{4}$

axis $x = 0$

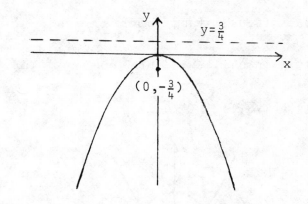

12. $y^2 = -x = 4(-\frac{1}{4})x$

$c = -\frac{1}{4}, \quad F(-\frac{1}{4}, 0)$

directrix $x = \frac{1}{4}$

axis $y = 0$

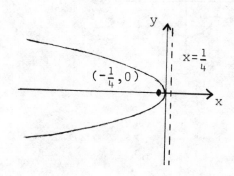

13. $(0,0), (\frac{1}{4}, 1)$

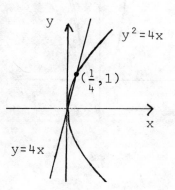

14. $(0,0), (-8, -16)$

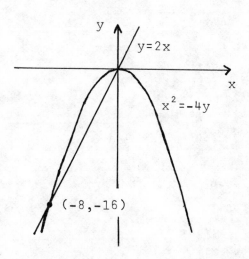

15. $(0,0)$, (ab, a^2b)

16. $(0,0)$, $(-ab, -a^2b)$

17. $(0,0)$, $(b/a^2, b/a)$

18. $(0,0)$, $(-b/a^2, -b/a)$

19. $(\sqrt{3}, 1)$, $(-\sqrt{3}, 1)$

20. $(0,0)$, $(-4, 2)$

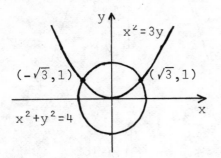

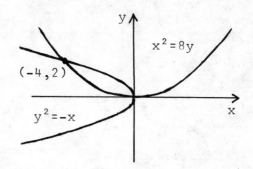

21. $(0,0)$, $(b^{\frac{2}{3}} a^{\frac{1}{3}}, b^{\frac{1}{3}} a^{\frac{2}{3}})$

22. $y = 4x - 2$

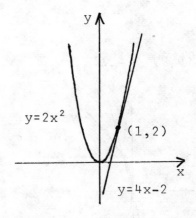

23. $y = 2ax - a$

SECTION 7.3

1. (a) $(x - 3)^2 + y^2 = 4$ (b) $(x - 3)^2 + (y + 5)^2 = 4$

    (c) $(x + 3)^2 + y^2 = 4$ (d) $(x + 3)^2 + (y - 5)^2 = 4$

2. (a) $(x - 5)^2 + (y + 10)^2 = 4$ (b) $(x + 5)^2 + (y - 10)^2 = 4$

    (c) $(x + 5)^2 + (y + 10)^2 = 4$ (d) $(x - 10)^2 + (y - 5)^2 = 4$

3. (a) $(y - 7)^2 = -6(x + 2)$ (b) $(y + 2)^2 = -6(x - 7)$

    (c) $y^2 = 6x$ (d) $x^2 = -6y$

4. (a) $y^2 = 2(x - 1)$ (b) $2y = 4x^2 - 1$

    vertex $(1,0)$, focus $(\frac{3}{2},0)$ vertex $(0,-\frac{1}{2})$,

    axis $y = 0$ focus $(0,-\frac{3}{8})$, axis $x = 0$

    directrix $x = \frac{1}{2}$ directrix $y = -\frac{5}{8}$

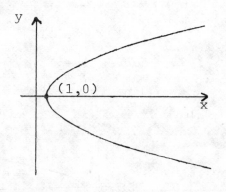

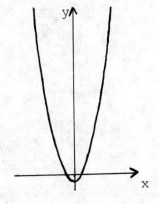

(c) $(x + 2)^2 = 8y - 12$

    vertex $(-2, \frac{3}{2})$

    focus $(-2, \frac{7}{2})$, axis $x = -2$

    directrix $y = -\frac{1}{2}$

(d) $y - 3 = 2(x - 1)^2$

    vertex $(1, 3)$

    focus $(1, \frac{25}{8})$, axis $x = 1$

    directrix $y = \frac{23}{8}$

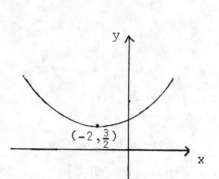

(e) $y = x^2 + x + 1$

    vertex $(-\frac{1}{2}, \frac{3}{4})$

    focus $(-\frac{1}{2}, 1)$, axis $x = -\frac{1}{2}$

    directrix $y = \frac{1}{2}$

(f) $x = y^2 + y + 1$

    vertex $(\frac{3}{4}, -\frac{1}{2})$

    focus $(1, -\frac{1}{2})$, axis $y = -\frac{1}{2}$

    directrix $x = \frac{1}{2}$

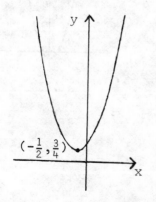

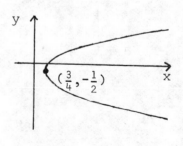

5. (a) $(x - 1)^2 = 4(y - 2)$ (b) $(x - 1)^2 = 4y$

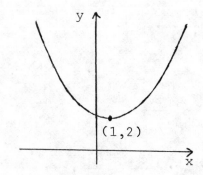

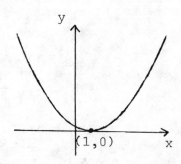

(c) $(y - 1)^2 = -2(x - \frac{3}{2})$ (d) $(y + 2)^2 = -6(x - \frac{7}{2})$

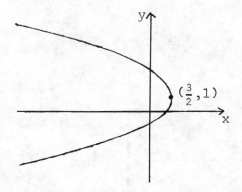

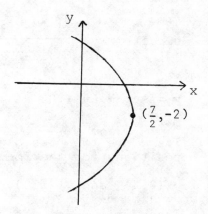

6. $(1,1)$, $(1,-1)$ 7. $(5,2)$, $(\frac{5}{4},-\frac{1}{2})$

8. $(0,-5)$, $(3,4)$, $(-3,4)$

9. (a) vertex (x_0,y_0) (b) vertex (x_0,y_0)

    focus $(x_0,y_0 + c)$ focus $(x_0 + c, y_0)$

    directrix $y = y_0 - c$ directrix $x = x_0 - c$

10. The parabola $(x - x_0)^2 = 4c(y - y_0)$ has vertex (x_0, y_0), focus $(x_0, y_0 + c)$, and directrix $y = y_0 - c$.

$$y = Ax^2 + Bx + C$$

$$x^2 + \frac{B}{A}x + \frac{C}{A} = \frac{y}{A}$$

$$x^2 + \frac{B}{A}x + \frac{B^2}{4A^2} = \frac{y}{A} - \frac{C}{A} + \frac{B^2}{4A^2}$$

$$[x - (-\frac{B}{2A})]^2 = 4(\frac{1}{4A})[y - \frac{4AC - B^2}{4A}]$$

$$\text{vertex } (-\frac{B}{2A}, \frac{4AC - B^2}{4A}), \quad \text{focus } (-\frac{B}{2A}, \frac{4AC - B^2 + 1}{4A})$$

$$\text{directrix } y = \frac{4AC - B^2 - 1}{4A}$$

11. $x = Ay^2 + By + C$, $A \neq 0$

12. There are two possible positions for the focus:

   $(2,2)$ and $(2,10)$.

   These in turn give rise to two parabolas:

   $2y = x^2 - 4x + 7$

   and

   $18y = x^2 - 4x + 103$.

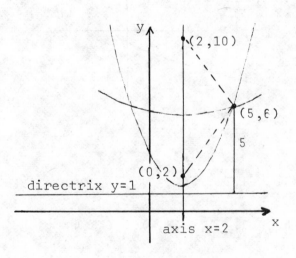

13. $144x = -5y^2 + 10y - 149$

14. $y = 2x - 3$

SECTION 7.4

1. $\dfrac{x^2}{9} + \dfrac{y^2}{4} = 1$

    (a) C(0,0)   (b) foci $(\pm\sqrt{5},0)$

    (c) length of major axis 6

    (d) length of minor axis 4

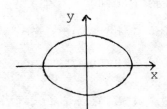

2. $\dfrac{x^2}{4} + \dfrac{y^2}{9} = 1$

    (a) C(0,0)   (b) foci $(0,\pm\sqrt{5})$

    (c) length of major axis 6

    (d) length of minor axis 4

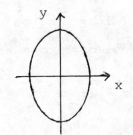

3. $3x^2 + 2y^2 = 12$

    (a) C(0,0)   (b) foci $(0,\pm\sqrt{2})$

    (c) length of major axis $2\sqrt{6}$

    (d) length of minor axis 4

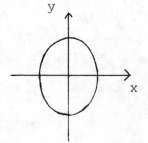

4. $(x - 1)^2 + 4y^2 = 64$

    (a) C(1,0)

    (b) foci $(1\pm 4\sqrt{3},0)$

    (c) length of major
        axis 16

    (d) length of minor
        axis 8

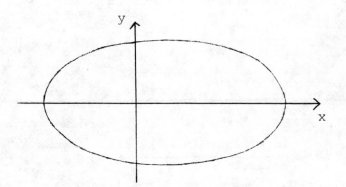

5. $3x^2 + 4y^2 - 12 = 0$

    (a) $C(0,0)$ (b) foci $(\pm 1, 0)$

    (c) length of major axis 4

    (d) length of minor axis $2\sqrt{3}$

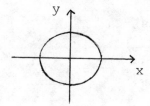

6. $4x^2 + y^2 - 6y + 5 = 0$

    (a) $C(0,3)$ (b) foci $(0, 3 \pm \sqrt{3})$

    (c) length of major axis 4

    (d) length of minor axis 2

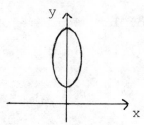

7. $4(x - 1)^2 + y^2 = 64$

    (a) $C(1,0)$ (b) foci $(1, \pm 4\sqrt{3})$

    (c) length of major axis 16

    (d) length of minor axis 8

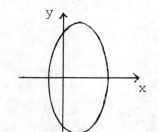

8. $16(x - 2)^2 + 25(y - 3)^2 = 400$

    (a) $C(2,3)$

    (b) foci $(5,3)$, $(-1,3)$

    (c) length of major axis 10

    (d) length of minor axis 8

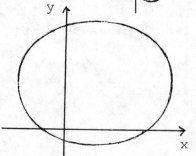

9. $\dfrac{x^2}{9} + \dfrac{y^2}{8} = 1$

10. $\dfrac{x^2}{8} + \dfrac{y^2}{9} = 1$

11. $\dfrac{(x - 6)^2}{25} + \dfrac{(y - 1)^2}{16} = 1$

12. $\dfrac{(x - 1)^2}{7} + \dfrac{(y - 6)^2}{25} = 1$

13. $\dfrac{(x - 1)^2}{21} + \dfrac{(y - 3)^2}{25} = 1$

14. $(x - 2)^2 + \dfrac{(y - 1)^2}{25} = 1$

15. $\dfrac{(x - 3)^2}{25} + \dfrac{(y + 1)^2}{9} = 1$

16. $(\pm 1, \pm 2)$

17. $(\pm 2\sqrt{2}, 2)$

18. $(-3, 2)$ and $(\dfrac{3}{5}, -\dfrac{14}{5})$

19. $3/5$

20. $4/5$

21. $\dfrac{x^2}{169} + \dfrac{y^2}{144} = 1$

22. $\dfrac{x^2}{169} + \dfrac{y^2}{25} = 1$

23. (a) Set $P = P(x,y)$. Then

$$d(P,F) = \sqrt{(x - c)^2 + y^2} \quad \text{and} \quad d(P,\ell) = \left| x - \frac{c}{e^2} \right|.$$

In terms of x and y, the equation $d(P,F) = e\, d(P,\ell)$ reads

$$\sqrt{(x - c)^2 + y^2} = e\left| x - \frac{c}{e^2} \right|.$$

Square both sides and simplify, and you'll find that this last equation reduces to

$$\frac{x^2}{(c/e)^2} + \frac{y^2}{(c/e)^2 - c^2} = 1.$$

This is the equation of an ellipse with major axis $2c/e$ and foci at $(-c,0)$, $(c,0)$. The eccentricity of the ellipse is

$$\frac{2c}{2c/e} = e.$$

(b) Take $e = c/a$, place F at $(c,0)$ and let ℓ be the line with equation $x = a^2/c$.

SECTION 7.5

1. $\dfrac{x^2}{9} - \dfrac{y^2}{16} = 1$

2. $\dfrac{x^2}{25} - \dfrac{y^2}{144} = 1$

3. $\dfrac{y^2}{25} - \dfrac{x^2}{144} = 1$

4. $\dfrac{y^2}{144} - \dfrac{x^2}{25} = 1$

5. $\dfrac{x^2}{9} - \dfrac{(y-1)^2}{16} = 1$

6. $\dfrac{(x-2)^2}{9} - \dfrac{(y-1)^2}{16} = 1$

7. $16y^2 - \dfrac{16}{15}(x+1)^2 = 1$

8. center $(0,0)$

   transverse axis 2

   vertices $(\pm 1, 0)$

   foci $(\pm\sqrt{2}, 0)$

   asymptotes $y = \pm x$

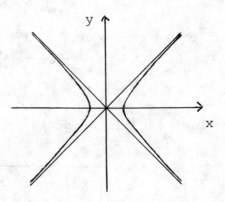

9. center $(0,0)$

   transverse axis 2

   vertices $(0, \pm 1)$

   foci $(0, \pm\sqrt{2})$

   asymptotes $y = \pm x$

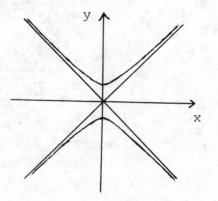

10. center $(0,0)$

   transverse axis 6

   vertices $(\pm 3, 0)$

   foci $(\pm 5, 0)$

   asymptotes $y = \pm\frac{4}{3}x$

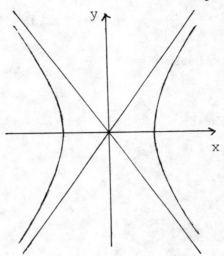

11. center $(0,0)$

   transverse axis 8

   vertices $(\pm 4, 0)$

   foci $(\pm 5, 0)$

   asymptotes $y = \pm\frac{3}{4}x$

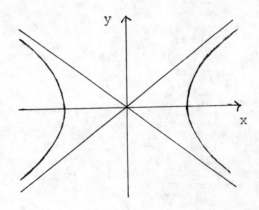

12. center $(0,0)$

   transverse axis 8

   vertices $(0, \pm 4)$

   foci $(0, \pm 5)$

   asymptotes $y = \pm\frac{4}{3}x$

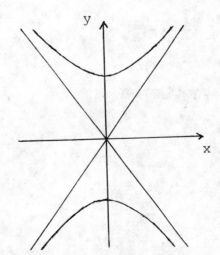

13. center $(0,0)$

 transverse axis 6

 vertices $(0,\pm 3)$

 foci $(0,\pm 5)$

 asymptotes $y = \pm\frac{3}{4}x$

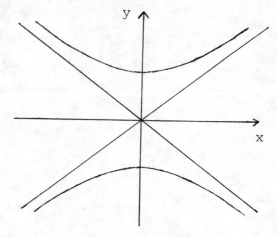

14. center $(1,3)$

 transverse axis 6

 vertices $(4,3)$, $(-2,3)$

 foci $(6,3)$, $(-4,3)$

 asymptotes $y = 3 \pm \frac{4}{3}(x-1)$

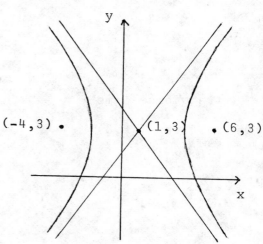

15. center $(1,3)$

 transverse axis 8

 vertices $(5,3)$, $(-3,3)$

 foci $(6,3)$, $(-4,3)$

 asymptotes $y = 3 \pm \frac{3}{4}(x-1)$

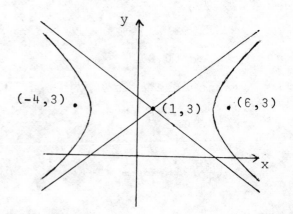

16. center (-1,2)

transverse axis 6

vertices (-4,2), (2,2)

foci (-1-$\sqrt{13}$,2),

(-1+$\sqrt{13}$,2)

asymptotes $y = \frac{2}{3}x + \frac{8}{3}$,

$y = -\frac{2}{3}x + \frac{4}{3}$

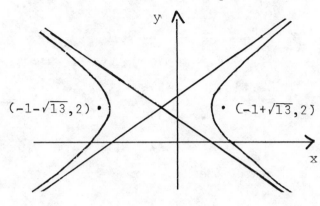

17. center (-1,2)

transverse axis 4

vertices (-3,2), (1,2)

foci (-1-$\sqrt{13}$,2),

(-1+$\sqrt{13}$,2)

asymptotes $y = \frac{3}{2}x + \frac{7}{2}$,

$y = -\frac{3}{2}x + \frac{1}{2}$

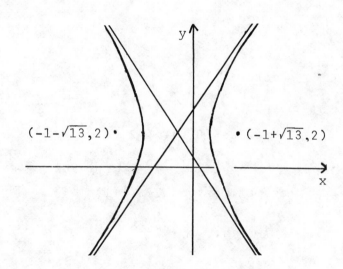

18. center (1,-2)

transverse axis 4

vertices (1,-4), (1,0)

foci (1,-2-$\sqrt{13}$),

(1,-2+$\sqrt{13}$)

asymptotes $y = \frac{2}{3}x - \frac{8}{3}$,

$y = -\frac{2}{3}x - \frac{4}{3}$

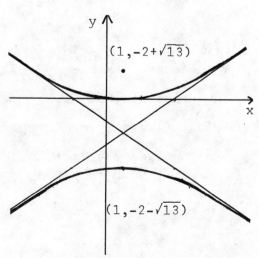

19. center $(1,-2)$

    transverse axis 6

    vertices $(1,-5)$, $(1,1)$

    foci $(1,-2-\sqrt{13})$,

    　　　$(1,-2+\sqrt{13})$

    asymptotes $y = \frac{3}{2}x - \frac{7}{2}$,

    　　　　　$y = -\frac{3}{2}x - \frac{1}{2}$

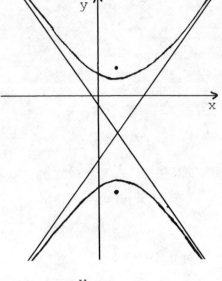

20. center $(-1,0)$

    transverse axis 2

    vertices $(0,0)$, $(-2,0)$

    foci $(1,0)$, $(-3,0)$

    asymptotes $y = \pm\sqrt{3}(x+1)$

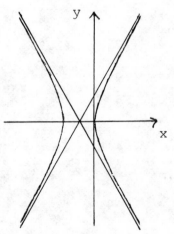

21. center $(1,3)$

    transverse axis 4

    vertices $(1,5)$, $(1,1)$

    foci $(1,3 \pm \sqrt{5})$

    asymptotes $y = 2x + 1$

    　　　　　$y = -2x + 5$

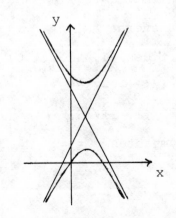

22. $e = \dfrac{13}{12}$

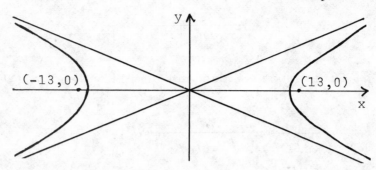

23. $e = \dfrac{13}{5}$

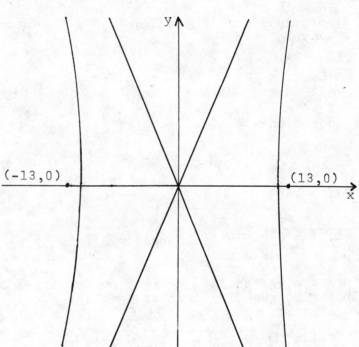

24. $\dfrac{x^2}{9} - \dfrac{y^2}{16} = 1$ 25. $\dfrac{x^2}{16} - \dfrac{y^2}{9} = 1$

26. (a) Set $P = P(x,y)$. Then

$$d(P,F) = \sqrt{(x-c)^2 + y^2} \quad \text{and} \quad d(P,\ell) = \left| x - \dfrac{c}{e^2} \right|$$

In terms of x and y, the equation

$$d(P,F) = e\, d(P,\ell)$$

reads

$$\sqrt{(x-c)^2 + y^2} = e\left|x - \frac{c}{e^2}\right| .$$

Square both sides and simplify, and you'll find that the last equation reduces to

$$\frac{x^2}{(c/e)^2} - \frac{y^2}{c^2 - (c/e)^2} = 1.$$

This is an equation of a hyperbola with transverse axis $2c/e$ and foci at $(-c,0)$, $(c,0)$. The eccentricity of the hyperbola is

$$\frac{2c}{2c/e} = e.$$

(b) Take $e = c/a$, place F at $(c,0)$ and let ℓ be the line with equation $x = a^2/c$.

SECTION 7.6

1. $\sqrt{(x-4)^2 + y^2} = |y+2|$ which simplifies to $4y = x^2 - 8x + 12$

2. Since the vertex lies halfway between the focus and the directrix, the directrix is the line $y = 12$. The parabola has equation

$$\sqrt{(x-4)^2 + y^2} = |y-12|$$

which can be written

$$24y = -x^2 + 8x + 128.$$

3. $\dfrac{x^2}{81} + \dfrac{y^2}{4} = 1$

4. $\dfrac{(x-2)^2}{4} + \dfrac{(y-1)^2}{81} = 1$

5. $4x^2 - \dfrac{4}{3}y^2 = 1$

6. $4y^2 - \dfrac{4}{3}x^2 = 1$

7. parabola with vertex at $(0,-1)$, focus at the origin

8. ellipse with foci at $(0,\pm1)$ and major axis $2\sqrt{3}$

9. hyperbola with foci at $(5,\pm2\sqrt{5})$ and transverse axis 4

10. hyperbola with foci at $(1\pm\sqrt{13},-1)$ and transverse axis 4

11. ellipse with foci at $(-3\pm\frac{1}{3}\sqrt{6},0)$ and major axis 2

12. parabola with vertex at $(5,2)$ and focus at $(5,4)$

13. parabola with vertex at $(\frac{3}{2},-2)$ and focus at $(1,-2)$

14. ellipse with foci at $(1,1\pm\sqrt{5})$ and major axis 6

15. ellipse with foci at $(\pm\frac{4}{15},-2)$ and major axis $\frac{2}{3}$

16. hyperbola with foci at $(-3,7\pm2\sqrt{2})$ and transverse axis $2\sqrt{7}$

17. hyperbola with foci at $(-1\pm\frac{6}{7}\sqrt{21},-4)$ and transverse axis $\frac{6}{7}\sqrt{35}$

18. hyperbola with foci at $(-\sqrt{3}\pm\sqrt{5},-\sqrt{3})$ and transverse axis $2\sqrt{3}$

19. the union of the parabola $x^2 = 4y$ and the ellipse $\dfrac{x^2}{9} + \dfrac{y^2}{4} = 1$

20. the union of the parabola $x^2 = 4y$ and the hyperbola $x^2 - 4y^2 = 1$

21. The equation for E can be written

$$\frac{x^2}{a^2} + \frac{(ay/b)^2}{a^2} = 1.$$

Thus E consists of all points (x,y) with $(x,ay/b) \in C$. In other words, E consists of all points $(x,by/a)$ with $(x,y) \in C$.

(over)

This means that E is the circle C with all vertical separations altered by a factor of b/a. One could therefore guess that

$$\text{area of E} = \frac{b}{a}(\text{area of C}) = \frac{b}{a}(\pi a^2) = \pi ab.$$

This formula is confirmed by calculus.

SECTION 8.1

1 - 8

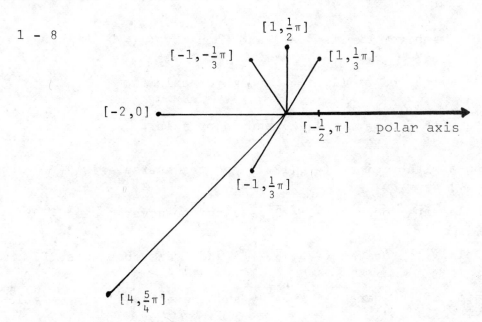

$[1, \frac{1}{2}\pi]$

$[-1, -\frac{1}{3}\pi]$

$[1, \frac{1}{3}\pi]$

$[-2, 0]$

$[-\frac{1}{2}, \pi]$ polar axis

$[-1, \frac{1}{3}\pi]$

$[4, \frac{5}{4}\pi]$

9. $(0,3)$ 10. $(2\sqrt{3}, 2)$ 11. $(1,0)$ 12. $(-\frac{1}{2}\sqrt{2}, -\frac{1}{2}\sqrt{2})$

13. $(-\frac{3}{2}, \frac{3}{2}\sqrt{3})$ 14. $(2,0)$ 15. $(-2,0)$ 16. $(0,-3)$

17. $[1, \frac{1}{2}\pi + 2n\pi]$, $[-1, \frac{3}{2}\pi + 2n\pi]$ 18. $[1, 2n\pi]$, $[-1, \pi + 2n\pi]$

19. $[3, \pi + 2n\pi]$, $[-3, 2n\pi]$ 20. $[4\sqrt{2}, \frac{1}{4}\pi + 2n\pi]$, $[-4\sqrt{2}, \frac{5}{4}\pi + 2n\pi]$

21. $[2\sqrt{2}, \frac{7}{4}\pi + 2n\pi]$, $[-2\sqrt{2}, \frac{3}{4}\pi + 2n\pi]$

22. $[6, \frac{5}{3}\pi + 2n\pi]$, $[-6, \frac{2}{3}\pi + 2n\pi]$ 23. $[8, \frac{1}{6}\pi + 2n\pi]$, $[-8, \frac{7}{6}\pi + 2n\pi]$

24. $[2, \frac{11}{6}\pi + 2n\pi]$, $[-2, \frac{5}{6}\pi + 2n\pi]$ 25. $[2, \frac{2}{3}\pi + 2n\pi]$, $[-2, \frac{5}{3}\pi + 2n\pi]$

26. (a) In rectangular coordinates the points can be written

$(r_1 \cos \theta_1, r_1 \sin \theta_1)$ and $(r_2 \cos \theta_2, r_2 \sin \theta_2)$.

The distance between these points is

$$\sqrt{r_1 \cos \theta_1 - r_2 \cos \theta_2)^2 + (r_1 \sin \theta_1 - r_2 \sin \theta_2)^2},$$

which can be simplified as follows:

$$\sqrt{r_1^2 \cos^2\theta_1 - 2r_1 r_2 \cos \theta_1 \cos \theta_2 + r_2^2 \cos^2\theta_2 + r_1^2 \sin^2\theta_1 - 2r_1 r_2 \sin \theta_1 \sin \theta_2 + r_2^2 \sin^2\theta_2} =$$

$$\sqrt{r_1^2(\cos^2\theta_1 + \sin^2\theta_1) + r_2^2(\cos^2\theta_2 + \sin^2\theta_2) - 2r_1 r_2(\cos \theta_1 \cos \theta_2 + \sin \theta_1 \sin \theta_2)} =$$

$$\sqrt{r_1^2 + r_2^2 - 2r_1 r_2 \cos (\theta_1 - \theta_2)}.$$

(b) The law of cosines can be written

$$d^2 = r_1^2 + r_2^2 - 2r_1 r_2 \cos (\theta_1 - \theta_2)$$

or, equivalently,

$$d = \sqrt{r_1^2 + r_2^2 - 2r_1 r_2 \cos (\theta_1 - \theta_2)}.$$

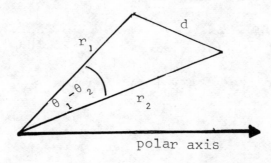

polar axis

202 / Section 8.2

SECTION 8.2

1. (a) $[\frac{1}{2}, \frac{11}{6}\pi]$ (b) $[\frac{1}{2}, \frac{5}{6}\pi]$ (c) $[\frac{1}{2}, \frac{7}{6}\pi]$

2. (a) $[3, \frac{5}{4}\pi]$ (b) $[3, \frac{1}{4}\pi]$ (c) $[3, \frac{7}{4}\pi]$

3. (a) $[2, \frac{2}{3}\pi]$ (b) $[2, \frac{5}{3}\pi]$ (c) $[2, \frac{1}{3}\pi]$

4. (a) $[3, \frac{3}{4}\pi]$ (b) $[3, \frac{7}{4}\pi]$ (c) $[3, \frac{1}{4}\pi]$

5. symmetry about the x-axis

6. symmetry about both axes and the origin

7. no symmetry about the coordinate axes; no symmetry about the origin

8. symmetry about both axes and the origin

9. symmetry about the origin

10. symmetry about both axes and the origin

11. $r^2 \sin 2\theta = 1$

12. $m = \tan \theta$

13. $r = 2$

14. $r = 2b \sin \theta$

15. $r = a(1 - \cos \theta)$

16. $r^2 = a^2 \cos 2\theta$

17. the horizontal line y = 4

18. the vertical line x = 4

19. the line $y = \sqrt{3}x$

20. the lines $y = \pm\sqrt{3}x$

21. the parabola $y^2 = 4(x + 1)$

22.
$$r = 4 \sin (\theta + \pi) = -4 \sin \theta$$
$$r^2 = -4r \sin \theta$$
$$x^2 + y^2 = -4y$$
$$x^2 + y^2 + 4y = 0$$
$$x^2 + (y + 2)^2 = 4$$

Answer: the circle $x^2 + (y + 2)^2 = 4$

SECTION 8.3

1. circle of radius 2 centered at the pole

2. circle of radius 3 centered at the pole

3. line through the pole with inclination 30°

4. line through the pole with inclination 150°

5. spiral

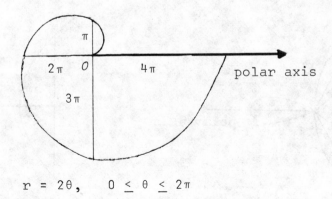

$$r = 2\theta, \quad 0 \le \theta \le 2\pi$$

6. spiral

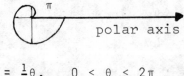

$$r = \tfrac{1}{2}\theta, \qquad 0 \le \theta \le 2\pi$$

7. circle of radius $\frac{1}{2}$ centered at $(\frac{1}{2},0)$

8. circle of radius $\frac{1}{2}$ centered at $(0,\frac{1}{2})$

9. circle of radius 1 centered at $(1,0)$

10. circle of radius 1 centered at $(0,1)$

11.

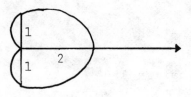

12.

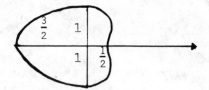

13. three leaved rose

14. parabola

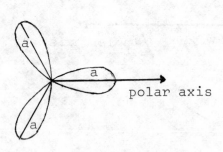

$$r = a \cos 3\theta$$

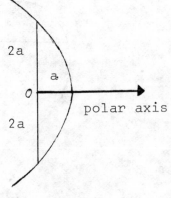

$$r = a \sec^2 \tfrac{1}{2}\theta$$

15. four-leaved rose

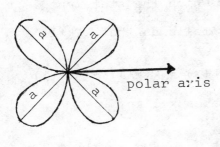

r = a sin 2θ

16. four-leaved rose

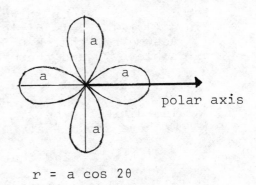

r = a cos 2θ

17. two-leaved lemniscate

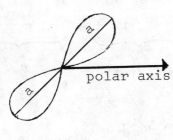

$r^2 = a^2 \sin 2\theta$

18. eight-leaved rose

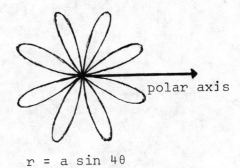

r = a sin 4θ

19. (a) parabola with directrix x = -d and focus at the origin

(b) an ellipse of eccentricity e

(c) a hyperbola of eccentricity e

SECTION 8.4

1. Let S be the set of integers for which the statement is true.
    Since (1)(2) = 2 is divisible by 2, 1 ε S.
        Assume now that k ε S. This tells us that k(k+1) is
    divisible by 2 and therefore

    $$(k+1)[(k+1) + 1] = (k+1)(k+2) = k(k+1) + 2(k+1)$$

    is also divisible by 2. This places k+1 in S.
        We have shown that

    $$1 \; ε \; S \qquad \text{and that} \qquad k \; ε \; S \qquad → \qquad k+1 \; ε \; S.$$

    It follows that S contains all the positive integers.

2. Let S be the set of integers for which the statement is true.
    Since (1)(2)(3) = 6 is divisible by 6, 1 ε S.
        Assume now that k ε S and note that

    $$(k+1)[(k+1) + 1][(k+1) + 2] = (k+1)(k+2)(k+3)$$

    $$= \underbrace{k(k+1)(k+2)}_{(*)} + \underbrace{3(k+1)(k+2)}_{(**)}.$$

    Expression (*) is divisible by 6 because k ε S; (**) is
    divisible by 6 because either k+1 or k+2 is even. This shows
    that

    $$(k+1)[(k+1) + 1][(k+1) + 2]$$

    is divisible by 6 and places k+1 in S.
        We have shown that

    $$1 \; ε \; S \qquad \text{and that} \qquad k \; ε \; S \qquad → \qquad k+1 \; ε \; S.$$

    It follows that S contains all the positive integers.

3. Use

    $$1 + 2 + \cdots + k + (k+1) = (1 + 2 + \cdots + k) + (k+1)$$

    $$= \frac{1}{2}k(k+1) + (k+1)$$

    $$= (k+1)(\frac{1}{2}k+1)$$

    $$= \frac{1}{2}(k+1)(k+2) = \frac{1}{2}(k+1)[(k+1)+ 1].$$

4. Use

$$1 + 3 + \cdots + (2k-1) + [2(k+1) - 1] = k^2 + [2(k+1) - 1]$$
$$= k^2 + 2k + 1 = (k+1)^2$$

5. Use

$$1^2 + 2^2 + \cdots + k^2 + (k+1)^2 = \frac{1}{6}k(k+1)(2k+1) + (k+1)^2$$
$$= \frac{1}{6}[k(k+1)(2k+1) + 6(k+1)^2]$$
$$= \frac{1}{6}(k+1)[k(2k+1) + 6(k+1)]$$
$$= \frac{1}{6}(k+1)[2k^2 + k + 6k + 6]$$
$$= \frac{1}{6}(k+1)[2k^2 + 7k + 6]$$
$$= \frac{1}{6}(k+1)(k+2)(2k+3)$$
$$= \frac{1}{6}(k+1)[(k+1) + 1][2(k+1) + 1].$$

6. Use

$$1^3 + 2^3 + \cdots + k^3 + (k+1)^3 = (1 + 2 + \cdots + k)^2 + (k+1)^3$$

exercise 3 ———→

$$= [\frac{1}{2}k(k+1)]^2 + (k+1)^3$$
$$= \frac{1}{4}k^2(k+1)^2 + (k+1)^3$$
$$= \frac{1}{4}[k^2(k+1)^2 + 4(k+1)^3]$$
$$= \frac{1}{4}(k+1)^2[k^2 + 4(k+1)]$$
$$= \frac{1}{4}(k+1)^2(k^2 + 4k + 4)$$
$$= \frac{1}{4}(k+1)^2(k+2)^2$$
$$= \frac{1}{4}(k+1)^2[(k+1) + 1]^2$$
$$= \{\frac{1}{2}(k+1)[(k+1) + 1]\}^2$$

exercise 3 ———→

$$= [1 + 2 + \cdots + k + (k+1)]^2.$$

7. Use $3^{2(k+1)+1} + 2^{(k+1)+2} = 3^{2k+3} + 2^{k+3}$

$$= 9(3^{2k+1}) + 2(2^{k+2})$$

$$= 7(3^{2k+1}) + 2[3^{2k+1} + 2^{k+2}].$$

8. True for all nonnegative integers.
   Outline of proof:

   Obviously not true for n negative.
   True for n = 0:
   $$9^0 - 8(0) - 1 = 1 - 0 - 1 = 0.$$

   true for n = 1:
   $$9^1 - 8(1) - 1 = 9 - 8 - 1 = 0.$$

   Assume true for k and use

   $$9^{k+1} - 8(k+1) - 1 = 9(9^k) - 8k - 9$$
   $$= 9(9^k) - 9(8k) - 9 + 64$$
   $$= 9(9^k - 8k - 1) + 64.$$

9. To go from k to k+1, take

   $$A = \{a_1, \cdots, a_{k+1}\} \quad \text{and} \quad B = \{a_1, \cdots, a_k\}.$$
   Assume that B has 2^k subsets:

   $$B_1, B_2, \cdots, B_{2^k}.$$
   The subsets of A are then

   $$B_1, B_2, \cdots, B_{2^k}$$
   together with

   $$B_1 \cup \{a_{k+1}\}, B_2 \cup \{a_{k+1}\}, \cdots, B_{2^k} \cup \{a_{k+1}\}.$$
   This gives $2(2^k) = 2^{k+1}$ subsets for A.

10. By exerecise 6 and exercise 3

$$1^3 + 2^3 + \cdots + (n-1)^3 = [\tfrac{1}{2}(n-1)n]^2 = \tfrac{1}{4}(n-1)^2 n^2 < \tfrac{1}{4}n^4$$

and

$$1^3 + 2^3 + \cdots + n^3 = [\tfrac{1}{2}n(n+1)]^2 = \tfrac{1}{4}n^2(n+1)^2 > \tfrac{1}{4}n^4.$$

11. For all positive integers $n \geq 2$,

$$(1 - \tfrac{1}{2})(1 - \tfrac{1}{3}) \cdots (1 - \tfrac{1}{n}) = \tfrac{1}{n}.$$

PROOF: Let S be the set of integers n for which the formula holds. Since

$$1 - \tfrac{1}{2} = \tfrac{1}{2},$$

$2 \; \varepsilon \; S.$
Suppose now that $k \; \varepsilon \; S$. This tells us that

$$(1 - \tfrac{1}{2})(1 - \tfrac{1}{3}) \cdots (1 - \tfrac{1}{k}) = \tfrac{1}{k}$$

and therefore that

$$(1 - \tfrac{1}{2})(1 - \tfrac{1}{3}) \cdots (1 - \tfrac{1}{k})(1 - \tfrac{1}{k+1}) = \tfrac{1}{k}(1 - \tfrac{1}{k+1})$$

$$= \tfrac{1}{k}(\tfrac{k}{k+1})$$

$$= \tfrac{1}{k+1}.$$

This places k+1 in S.
We have shown that

$$2 \; \varepsilon \; S \qquad \text{and that} \qquad k \; \varepsilon \; S \quad \rightarrow \quad k+1 \; \varepsilon \; S.$$

This tells us that all the integers greater than or equal to 2 are in S.

SECTION 8.5

1. $x = 3$, $y = 1$

2. $x = 0$, $y = 4$

3. $x = 2$, $y = 3$

4. $x = \frac{1}{2}$, $y = 0$

5. $x = -6$, $y = 4$

6. $x = \frac{33}{31}$, $y = -\frac{17}{31}$

7. $x = 1$, $y = 0$, $z = 1$

8. $x = 1$, $y = -2$, $z = -2$

9. $x = 0$, $y = 1$, $z = 2$

10. $x = 2$, $y = 2$, $z = 2$

11. $x = 1$, $y = -1$, $z = 2$

12. $x = -\frac{43}{6}$, $y = -\frac{130}{3}$, $z = -\frac{389}{9}$

SECTION 8.6

1. (a) - (h)

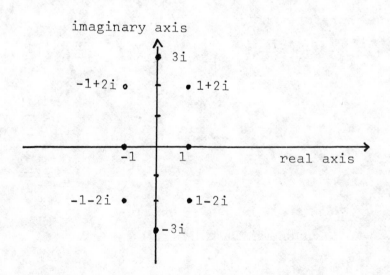

2. $8 - i$ 3. $2 + 3i$ 4. 1 5. $11 - 8i$

6. $17 - 7i$ 7. $13 + 13i$ 8. $18 - 38i$ 9. $-42 + 2i$

10. $-1 + 5i$ 11. $1 + 5i$ 12. $-i$ 13. 1

14. $(1 + i)^3 = 1 + 3i + 3i^2 + i^3 = 1 + 3i - 3 - i = -2 + 2i$

15. $(1 - i)^3 = 1 - 3i + 3i^2 - i^3 = 1 - 3i - 3 + i = -2 - 2i$

16. $(\frac{1}{2}\sqrt{2} + \frac{1}{2}\sqrt{2}i)^2 = (\frac{1}{2}\sqrt{2})^2 + 2(\frac{1}{2}\sqrt{2})(\frac{1}{2}\sqrt{2}i) + (\frac{1}{2}\sqrt{2}i)^2 = \frac{1}{2} + i - \frac{1}{2} = i$

17. $(\frac{1}{2}\sqrt{2} + \frac{1}{2}\sqrt{2}i)^4 = i^2 = -1$ by exercise 16

18. $\pm 3i$ 19. $-1 \pm 2\sqrt{2}i$ 20. $-\frac{1}{3} \pm \frac{1}{3}\sqrt{2}i$

21. $-\frac{1}{3} \pm \frac{1}{3}\sqrt{29}i$ 22. $-\frac{1}{2} \pm \frac{1}{2}i$ 23. $\frac{1}{10}(1 \pm \sqrt{139}i)$

24. and 25. routine

26.

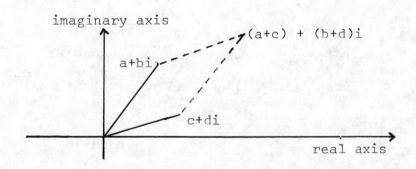

the parallelogram of addition

27. (a) $|z|$ is the distance from z to the origin

    (b) $|z_1 z_2| = |(a + bi)(c + di)|$

$$= |(ac - bd) + (ad + bc)i|$$

$$= \sqrt{(ac - bd)^2 + (ad + bc)^2}$$

$$= \sqrt{a^2c^2 - 2abcd + b^2d^2 + a^2d^2 + 2abcd + b^2c^2}$$

$$= \sqrt{a^2c^2 + a^2d^2 + b^2c^2 + b^2d^2}$$

$$= \sqrt{a^2(c^2 + d^2) + b^2(c^2 + d^2)}$$

$$= \sqrt{(a^2 + b^2)(c^2 + d^2)}$$

$$= \sqrt{a^2 + b^2} \sqrt{c^2 + d^2}$$

$$= |z_1||z_2|$$

28. (a)

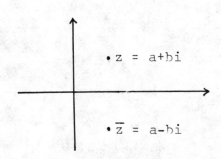

    (b) $|\bar{z}| = \sqrt{a^2 + (-b)^2} = \sqrt{a^2 + b^2} = |z|$

$$z\bar{z} = (a + bi)(a - bi) = a^2 + b^2 = (\sqrt{a^2 + b^2})^2 = |z|^2$$

29. Set
$$z = a + bi, \quad w_1 = c_1 + d_1 i, \quad w_2 = c_2 + d_2 i.$$
Since $z \neq 0$,

$$zw_1 = zw_2 \rightarrow (a + bi)(c_1 + d_1 i) = (a + bi)(c_2 + d_2 i)$$

$$\rightarrow (ac_1 - bd_1) + (ad_1 + bc_1)i = (ac_2 - bd_2)$$

$$+ (ad_2 + bc_2)i$$

$$\rightarrow \quad ac_1 - bd_1 = ac_2 - bd_2, \qquad ad_1 + bc_1 = ad_2 + bc_2$$

$$\rightarrow \quad \begin{aligned} (c_1 - c_2)a - (d_1 - d_2)b &= 0 \\ (d_1 - d_2)a + (c_1 - c_2)b &= 0. \end{aligned}$$

This is a pair of linear equations in a and b with determinant

$$(c_1 - c_2)^2 + (d_1 - d_2)^2.$$

If this determinant is not zero, the system has the unique solution

$$a = 0, \quad b = 0. \qquad \text{(Theorem 8.5.3)}$$

This violates our hypothesis that $z \neq 0$. It follows then that

$$(c_1 - c_2)^2 + (d_1 - d_2)^2 = 0.$$

This forces

$$c_1 = c_2, \quad d_1 = d_2$$

and shows that

$$w_1 = w_2.$$

30. For $z \neq 0$

$$z \cdot \frac{1}{z} = z \cdot \frac{\bar{z}}{|z|^2} = \frac{z\bar{z}}{|z|^2} = \frac{|z|^2}{|z|^2} = 1.$$

31. (a) $\dfrac{1}{i} = \dfrac{\bar{i}}{|i|^2} = \bar{i} = -i$

(b) $\dfrac{1}{1 + i} = \dfrac{\overline{1 + i}}{|1 + i|^2} = \dfrac{1 - i}{2} = \dfrac{1}{2} - \dfrac{1}{2}i$

(c) $\dfrac{1}{1 - i} = \dfrac{\overline{1 - i}}{|1 + i|^2} = \dfrac{1 + i}{2} = \dfrac{1}{2} + \dfrac{1}{2}i$

(d) $\dfrac{1}{2 + 3i} = \dfrac{\overline{2 + 3i}}{|2 + 3i|^2} = \dfrac{2 - 3i}{13} = \dfrac{2}{13} - \dfrac{3}{13}i$

32. (a) $\dfrac{i}{3 - 5i} = i \cdot \dfrac{i}{3 - 5i} = i \cdot \dfrac{3 + 5i}{34} = \dfrac{3i - 5}{34} = -\dfrac{5}{34} + \dfrac{3}{34}i$

(b) $\dfrac{3 + 2i}{2 + i} = (3 + 2i) \cdot \left(\dfrac{2 - i}{5}\right) = \dfrac{8 + i}{5} = \dfrac{8}{5} + \dfrac{1}{5}i$

(c) $\dfrac{2 + 5i}{5 - 2i} = (2 + 5i) \cdot \left(\dfrac{5 + 2i}{29}\right) = \dfrac{29i}{29} = i$

(d) $\dfrac{6 - 7i}{4 + 5i} = (6 - 7i) \cdot \left(\dfrac{4 - 5i}{41}\right) = \dfrac{-11 - 58i}{41} = -\dfrac{11}{41} - \dfrac{58}{41}i$